Poems for Seasons and Celebrations

Also edited by William Cole

POEMS OF MAGIC AND SPELLS

I WENT TO THE ANIMAL FAIR

STORY POEMS NEW AND OLD

HUMOROUS POETRY FOR CHILDREN

POEMS FOR
Seasons
AND
Celebrations

edited by WILLIAM COLE

illustrated by JOHANNES TROYER

THE WORLD PUBLISHING COMPANY
CLEVELAND AND NEW YORK

TO

Velma V. Varner

PUBLISHED BY The World Publishing Company

2231 WEST 110TH STREET, CLEVELAND 2, OHIO

PUBLISHED SIMULTANEOUSLY IN CANADA BY

NELSON, FOSTER & SCOTT LTD.

Library of Congress Catalog Card Number: 61-12012

FIRST EDITION

COHC

COPYRIGHT ACKNOWLEDGMENTS

The editor and The World Publishing Company herewith render thanks to the following authors, publishers, and agents whose interest, co-operation, and permission to reprint have made possible the preparation of *Poems for Seasons and Celebrations*. All possible care has been taken to trace the ownership of every selection included and to make full acknowledgment for its use. If any errors have accidentally occurred, they will be corrected in subsequent editions, provided notification is sent to the publisher.

Marnie Pomeroy Ackerman, for "April Fools' Day," "Ground Hog Day," "Hallowe'en," "January 1," and "Labor Day" by Marnie Pomeroy. Reprinted by permission of Marnie Pomeroy Ackerman.

Ballantine Books, Inc., for "The Pine Bough" by Richard Aldridge, from *New Poems by American Poets*, copyright, ©, 1953, Ballantine Books, Inc. Reprinted by permission of Richard Aldridge.

Brandt & Brandt, for "Abraham Lincoln" by Stephen Vincent Benét, from *A Book of Americans* by Rosemary and Stephen Vincent Benét, copyright, 1933, Rosemary and Stephen Vincent Benét, copyright renewed, 1961, Rosemary Carr Benét, published by Holt, Rinehart and Winston, Inc.; for "Listen to the People: Independence Day, 1941" from *Selected Works of Stephen Vincent Benét*, copyright, 1941, Stephen Vincent Benét, published by Holt, Rinehart and Winston, Inc. Reprinted by permission of Brandt & Brandt.

Peggy Bennett Cole, for "A Mother Is a Sun" by Peggy Bennett. Reprinted by permission of Peggy Bennett Cole.

Mitchell Donian, for "If someone asks you" by Mitchell Donian. Reprinted by permission of the author.

E. P. Dutton & Co., Inc. and Oxford University Press, for "Cows" and "Fireworks" from *The Blackbird in the Lilac* by James Reeves, copyright, ©, 1959, James Reeves. Reprinted by permission of E. P. Dutton & Co., Inc. and Oxford University Press.

Norma Millay Ellis, for "God's World" from *Collected Poems* by Edna St. Vincent Millay, copyright, 1913, 1941, Edna St. Vincent Millay, published by Harper & Brothers. Reprinted by permission of Norma Millay Ellis.

Margaret Fishback, for "Christmas Pageant," "Hallowe'en Indignation Meeting," "Kerchoo!" and "Triolet on a Dark Day" by Margaret Fishback. Reprinted by permission of the author.

Louis Ginsberg, for "To My Mother" by Louis Ginsberg, published by *The New York Times*. Reprinted by permission of the publisher and the author.

Mrs. Arthur Guiterman, for "Thanksgiving Wishes," "Twist-rime on Spring," and "Young Washington" by Arthur Guiterman. Reprinted by permission of Mrs. Arthur Guiterman.

Harcourt, Brace & World, Inc., for "Leetla Giorgio Washeenton" from *Selected Poems of T. A. Daly*, copyright, 1936, Harcourt, Brace & World, Inc.; for "Hallowe'en" from *The Little Hill* by Harry Behn, copyright, 1949, Harry Behn; for "Chanson Innocente" ("little tree") from *Poems 1923-1954* by E. E. Cummings, copyright, 1925, 1953, E. E. Cummings; for "Poem" ("maggie and milly and molly and may") from *95 Poems* by E. E. Cummings, copyright, ©, 1956, E. E. Cummings; for "Washington Monument by Night" from *Slabs of the Sunburnt West* by Carl Sandburg, copyright, 1922, Harcourt, Brace & World, Inc., copyright renewed, 1950, Carl Sandburg. Reprinted by permission of Harcourt, Brace & World, Inc.

Harper & Brothers, for "Midsummer Pause" from *Barnyard Year* by Fred Lape, copyright, 1950, Fred Lape. Reprinted by permission of Harper & Brothers.

Holt, Rinehart and Winston, Inc., for "Stopping by Woods on a Snowy Evening" from *Complete Poems of Robert Frost*, copyright, 1930, copyright renewed, 1949, Holt, Rinehart and Winston, Inc. Reprinted by permission of Holt, Rinehart and Winston, Inc.

Holt, Rinehart and Winston, Inc., The Society of Authors, and Messrs. Jonathan Cape Ltd., for "The Lent Lily" from *A Shropshire Lad* by A. E. Housman, copyright, 1924, copyright renewed, 1959, Holt, Rinehart and Winston, Inc. Reprinted by permission of Holt, Rinehart and Winston, Inc., The Society of Authors, and Messrs. Jonathan Cape Ltd.

Houghton Mifflin Company, for "The Brown Bear" from *Children Sing in the Far West* by Mary Austin. Reprinted by permission of Houghton Mifflin Company.

Alfred A. Knopf, Inc., for "Autumn" from *Kings, Lords, and Commons* by Frank O'Connor, copyright, 1939, Macmillan & Co. Ltd., London and St. Martin's Press, New York, copyright, ©, 1959, Frank O'Connor. Reprinted by permission of Alfred A. Knopf, Inc.

Newman Levy, for "Midsummer Fantasy" by Newman Levy. Reprinted by permission of the author.

J. B. Lippincott Company, for "Spring Song" from *Poems by a Little Girl* by Hilda Conkling, copyright, 1920, 1947, Hilda Conkling. Reprinted by permission of J. B. Lippincott Company.

J. B. Lippincott Company and Harold Ober Associates, Inc., for "Earth and Sky" from *Poems for Children* by Eleanor Farjeon, copyright, ©, 1927, 1951, 1955, Eleanor Farjeon. Reprinted by permission of J. B. Lippincott Company and Harold Ober Associates, Inc.

Little, Brown & Co., for "A Pavane for the Nursery" from *Poems, 1947-1957* by William Jay Smith, copyright, ©, 1957, William Jay Smith. Reprinted by permission of Little, Brown & Co.

The Macmillan Company, for "April" and "May Day" from *Collected Poems* by Sara Teasdale, copyright, 1915, The Macmillan Company, copyright renewed, 1943, Mamie T. Wheless; for "January" from *Twelve Months Make a Year* by Elizabeth Coatsworth, copyright, 1943, The Macmillan Company; for "Late October" from *Stars Tonight* by Sara Teasdale, copyright, 1930, The Macmillan Company, copyright renewed, 1958, Mamie T. Wheless; for "The Secret Heart" from *Strange Holiness* by Robert P. Tristram Coffin, copyright, 1935, The Macmillan Company; for "Something Told the Wild Geese" from *Poems* by Rachel Field, copyright, 1934, The Macmillan Company; for "Would I Might Rouse the Lincoln in You All" from "The Litany of Heroes" from *Collected Poems* by Vachel Lindsay, copyright, 1913, The Macmillan Company. Reprinted by permission of The Macmillan Company.

The Macmillan Company and Macmillan & Co. Ltd., for "White Fields" from *Collected Poems* by James Stephens, copyright, 1915, The Macmillan Company, copyright renewed, 1943, James Stephens. Reprinted by permission of The Macmillan Company, Macmillan & Co. Ltd., The Macmillan Co. of Canada Ltd., and Mrs. Iris Wise.

Ellen C. Masters, for "Anne Rutledge" from *Spoon River Anthology* by Edgar Lee Masters, published by The Macmillan Company, 1914, 1942. Reprinted by permission of Ellen C. Masters.

Harold Matson Company, for "Old Dan'l" from *Selected Poems* by L. A. G. Strong. Reprinted by permission of Harold Matson Company.

John Travers Moore, for "The Last Flower" by John Travers Moore. Reprinted by permission of the author.

Alice S. Morris, for "Mrs. Santa Claus' Christmas Present" by Alice S. Morris. Reprinted by permission of the author.

G. P. Putnam's Sons, for "Night and Morning" from *Everything and Anything* by Dorothy Aldis, copyright, 1925, 1926, 1927, Dorothy Aldis. Reprinted by permission of G. P. Putnam's Sons.

Rand McNally & Company, for "Simple Sam" from *The Peter Patter Book* by Leroy F. Jackson, copyright, 1918, copyright renewed, 1946, Rand McNally & Company. Reprinted by permission of Rand McNally & Company.

St. Martin's Press, Inc. and The Macmillan Co. of Canada Ltd., for "The Discovery" and "The March" from *Collected Poems* by J. C. Squire. Reprinted by permission of Mr. Raglan Squire, Macmillan & Co. Ltd., The Macmillan Co. of Canada Ltd., and St. Martin's Press, Inc.

Mrs. Lew Sarett, for "Four Little Foxes" from *Covenant with Earth* by Lew Sarett, edited and copyrighted, 1956, Alma Johnson Sarett, published by University of Florida Press, Gainesville, 1956. Reprinted by permission of Mrs. Lew Sarett.

Shelley Silverstein, for "The Flag," "George Washington," "I must remember," "If I Had a Firecracker," "Oh Did You Hear?" "On Halloween," "Peace and Joy," "There you sit," and "Valentine" by Shelley Silverstein. Reprinted by permission of the author.

Bradford Smith, for "Winter Is Icumen in" by Bradford Smith, from Martin Levin's Phoenix Nest, *Saturday Review*. Reprinted by permission of the author.

The Viking Press, Inc., for "Christmas Morning" and "Father's Story" from *Under the Tree* by Elizabeth Madox Roberts, copyright, 1922, B. W. Huebsch, Inc., copyright, 1950, Ivor S. Roberts. Reprinted by permission of The Viking Press, Inc.

The Viking Press, Inc. and Siegfried Sassoon, for "Everyone Sang" from *Collected Poems* by Siegfried Sassoon, copyright, 1920, E. P. Dutton & Co., Inc., copyright, 1948, Siegfried Sassoon. Reprinted by permission of The Viking Press, Inc. and Siegfried Sassoon.

Henry Z. Walck, Inc. and David Higham Associates Ltd., for "Good Bishop Valentine," "The Great Discovery," "October's Song," "Up the Hill, Down the Hill," and "Upon an Easter Morning" from *The Children's Bells* by Eleanor Farjeon, copyright, ©, 1960, Eleanor Farjeon. Reprinted by permission of Eleanor Farjeon, Henry Z. Walck, Inc., and David Higham Associates Ltd.

Mildred Weston, for "Father" by Mildred Weston. Reprinted by permission of the author.

Contents

MOTHER'S DAY

MEMORIAL DAY (DECORATION DAY)

FLAG DAY

FATHER'S DAY

SUMMER

Introduction

WOULDN'T YOU think poets would write their best poems about spring? I had thought so, because spring is the season when everything is fresh and baby green and people go around falling in love, and *everybody* feels like a poet. But it just isn't so. Do you know what season poets write the most poems—and the best poems—about? Winter. Dreary winter!

And why do poets write their best poems about winter? I can only assume that it's because winter is the season when man realizes how small and weak he really is, when the snow and the chill and the wind show him how powerful nature is. It is the season when man, stuck snug indoors most of the time, writes poems expressing his awe and admiration of nature's power.

The best poems in this collection are the ones about the seasons, not the holidays. Seasons are nature's celebrations; holidays are man's celebrations. Seasons are in the poet's blood: he blossoms in spring, is lazy and happy in summer, is a bit sad, yet brisk and snappy in autumn, and hibernates away from the weather in winter. Holidays celebrating patriots, battles, and flags don't mean so much to him; they're not so personal.

In searching for poems for this book, I found another thing that surprised me. Poets write their worst poems about Mother! I know that poets love their mothers, but

[17]

when they try putting their love down on paper, they get terribly soupy and sentimental. It's embarrassing. Most poets have pictured their mothers as old, bent, gray-haired, toil-worn women. The mothers *I* know, including my own, are lively, lovely, young-looking, and fun to be with. I had to search and search and search to find the few good poems about mothers for the book.

Holidays have always been celebrated in poetry, even in primitive days before there was any written communication. Way back then, people used to chant stories about battles and heroes, great hunts and good harvests. They chanted in rhythm, and the rhythm helped the younger people memorize the stories so that they could keep the legends alive and pass them on to their children. One thing I kept in mind while putting this book together was to choose a lot of poems that are good for reading aloud. Reading poetry aloud (and it isn't done nearly enough today) is the best way I know to celebrate a holiday or acknowledge the first day of a new season. But do remember, though, that before you read a poem aloud in front of an audience, you should try it out by yourself in private. You should go to a soundproof room or the top of a tree and have a rehearsal, just as actors do with their lines. In this way you'll learn how to get the most out of the poem: when to speak softly and when to shout, when to slow up and when to step on the gas. Some of the poems that are especially good to read aloud are Robert Frost's "Stopping by Woods on a Snowy Evening," Bliss Carman's "A Vagabond Song," Edna St. Vincent Millay's "God's World," Marnie Pomeroy's "Halloween," and, for Thanksgiving laughs, E. V. Wright's "When Father Carves the Duck."

[18]

Most of the poems in this collection are easy to read and understand, but I've included a few that you'll have to puzzle over; it's good exercise for the brain to work them out, and in my opinion, a difficult poem is much more rewarding to figure out than a mathematical problem. Some of the spellings in certain poems may seem strange, but that's because many of them were written over a century ago when such spellings were correct. The poem by William Barnes looks very odd—he was from Dorset, England, and wrote in the Dorset dialect, just as Robert Burns wrote many of his poems in Scottish dialect.

I hope you won't feel you have to wait for proper seasons or holidays to read the poems in this book; nobody will mind if you decide to read about Mother on Father's Day, about Lincoln on Washington's Birthday, or about winter in the middle of summer.

And right now is the time for me to celebrate the help and suggestions I had from Maria Cimino and Jean Meyer while putting this collection together, and to bow low in thanks to two poets, Marnie Pomeroy and Shelley Silverstein, who wrote some wonderful brand-new poems for it.

WILLIAM COLE

[19]

I must remember:

Turkey on Thanksgiving,
Pudding on Christmas,
Eggs on Easter,
Chicken on Sunday,
Fish on Friday—
But ah me I'm such a dunce,
I went and ate them all at once.

SHELLEY SILVERSTEIN

The Wassail Song

Here we come a-wassailing
  Among the leaves so green,
Here we come a-wandering
  So fair to be seen.

Love and joy come to you
  And to you your wassail too,
And God bless you, and send you
  A happy New Year.

We are not daily beggars
  That beg from door to door,
But we are neighbors' children
  That you have seen before.

Good Master and good Mistress,
    As you sit by the fire,
Pray think of us poor children
    Who are wandering in the mire.

Bring us out a table
    And spread it with a cloth;
Bring us out a mouldy cheese
    And some of your Christmas loaf.

God bless the master of this house,
    Likewise the mistress too;
And all the little children
    That round the table go.

OLD DEVONSHIRE CAROL

Happy New Year! Happy New Year!
I've come to wish you a Happy New Year.
I've got a little pocket and it is very thin,
Please give me a penny to put some money in.
If you haven't got a penny, a halfpenny will do,
If you haven't got a halfpenny, well—
        God Bless You!

ENGLISH CHILDREN'S RHYME

A New Year Carol

Here we bring new water
    from the well so clear,
For to worship God with,
    this happy New Year.
Sing levy dew, sing levy dew,
    the water and the wine;
The seven bright gold wires
      and the bugles that do shine.

Sing reign of Fair Maid,
    with gold upon her toe,—
Open you the West Door,
    and turn the Old Year go.

Sing reign of Fair Maid
    with gold upon her chin,—
Open you the East Door,
    and let the New Year in.
Sing levy dew, sing levy dew,
    the water and the wine;
The seven bright gold wires
      and the bugles they do shine.

ANONYMOUS

[23]

from *The Death of the Old Year*

Full knee-deep lies the winter snow,
    And the winter winds are wearily sighing:
Toll ye the church-bell sad and slow,
And tread softly, and speak low,
For the old year lies a-dying.
    Old year, you must not die;
    You came to us so readily,
    You lived with us so steadily,
    Old year, you shall not die.

. . .

He was full of joke and jest;
But all his merry quips are o'er:
To see him die, across the waste
His son and heir doth ride post-haste;
But he'll be dead before.
    Every one for his own.
    The night is starry and cold, my friend,
    And the New-year blithe and bold, my friend,
    Comes up to take his own.

How hard he breathes! over the snow
I heard just now the crowing cock.
The shadows flicker to and fro;
The cricket chirps; the light burns low:

'Tis nearly twelve o'clock.
  Shake hands, before you die.
  Old year, we'll dearly rue for you:
  What is it we can do for you?
  Speak out before you die.

His face is growing sharp and thin.
Alack! our friend is gone.
Close up his eyes: tie up his chin:
Step from the corpse, and let him in
That standeth there alone,
  And waiteth at the door.
  There's a new foot on the floor, my friend,
  And a new face at the door, my friend
  A new face at the door.

ALFRED, LORD TENNYSON

January 1

Our twelve months go round and round,
The same months every year.
And January starts them off,
The first day icy-clear.

Arise before the orange dawn
In morning's blue is lost.
Arise, enjoy your window panes
That glow with crusts of frost.

Enjoy the black trees lined with snow,
The meadow smooth and white
In last year's haggard countryside
That dazzles since the night.

Begin this year as though you too
Were really not the same—
Like every January first,
Brand-new in your old name.

MARNIE POMEROY

Up the Hill, Down the Hill

Old One, lie down,
Your journey is done,
Little New Year
Will rise with the sun.
Now you have come to
The foot of the hill,
Lay down your bones,
Old Year, and lie still.

Young One, step out,
Your journey's begun,
Weary Old Year
Makes way for his son.
Now you have started

To climb up the hill,
Put best foot forward,
New Year, with a will.

ELEANOR FARJEON

from *A New Year Idyl*

Upon this happy New Year night,
    A roach crawls up my pot of paste,
    And begs me for a tiny taste.
Aye, eat thy fill, for it is right
That while the rest of earth is glad,
    And bells are ringing wild and free,
    Thou shouldst not, gentle roachling, be
Forlorn and gaunt and weak and sad.

EUGENE FIELD

ROUND-HOG DAY

CANDLEMAS DAY

Ground Hog Day

In February when few gusty flakes
Above the frozen sheets of snow still hover,
Out of his hole the sleepy ground hog breaks
To peek around to see if winter's over.

Now if he finds his shadow, back he shies
To nap while deeper drifts the wind shall bring;
But if no shadow shows beneath dark skies
He waddles through the ditch to look for spring.

MARNIE POMEROY

[29]

If Candlemas Day be dry and fair,
The half o' winter's to come and mair;
If Candlemas Day be wet and foul,
The half o' winter's gone at Yule.

TRADITIONAL SCOTTISH RHYME

If Candlemas Day be fair and bright,
Winter will have another flight;
But if it be dark with clouds and rain,
Winter is gone, and will not come again.

TRADITIONAL SCOTTISH RHYME

INCOLN'S BIRTHDAY

Would I Might Rouse the Lincoln in You All

Would I might rouse the Lincoln in you all,
That which is gendered in the wilderness
From lonely prairies and God's tenderness.
Imperial soul, star of a weedy stream,
Born where the ghosts of buffaloes still gleam,
Whose spirit hoof-beats storm above his grave,
Above that breast of earth and prairie-fire—
Fire that freed the slave.

VACHEL LINDSAY

In Hardin County, 1809

With flintlocked guns and polished stocks,
Knee breeches and long homespun socks,
One morning of St. Valentine
Two hunters met in 1809.
Across the line from Illinois;
They stopped their mules and voiced their joy.

"Why, Ben, it's been quite a spell
Since I've seen you. The folks all well?
Bring any news from up near town?"
"Why, yes. D'you know John Ezry Brown?
They say that he's a-goin down
To Washington in all the din
To see Jim Madison sworn in.

"And this young feller Bonaparte
That's fightin' cross the sea,
Is slicin' Europe all to bits.
Least that's what they're a tellin' me."
"Wal, wal, nice day, kinda breezy,
This mule's gettin' quite uneasy.

"Now come and see us some time, do,
And bring the gals and Hepsy, too."
"Yes, some fine day we'll be along,
Got any news to send along?"

"No, nothin' worth a tinker's song.
There's nothin' happens here near me,
Doggondest place you ever see.

"Tom Lincoln lives right over there,
In that log cabin, bleak and bare,
They say they have a little babe,
I understand they've named him 'Abe.'
Yes, Sally said just 'tother day,
That nothin' happens down this way."

LULU E. THOMPSON

Anne Rutledge

Out of me unworthy and unknown
The vibrations of deathless music;
"With malice toward none, with charity for all."
Out of me the forgiveness of millions toward millions,
And the beneficent face of a nation
Shining with justice and truth.
I am Anne Rutledge who sleep beneath these weeds,
Beloved in life of Abraham Lincoln,
Wedded to him, not through union,
But through separation.
Bloom forever, O Republic,
From the dust of my bosom!

EDGAR LEE MASTERS

[33]

Abraham Lincoln
(1809-1865)

Lincoln was a long man.
He liked out of doors.
He liked the wind blowing
And the talk in country stores.

He liked telling stories,
He liked telling jokes.
"Abe's quite a character,"
Said quite a lot of folks.

Lots of folks in Springfield
Saw him every day,
Walking down the street
In his gaunt, long way.

Shawl around his shoulders,
Letters in his hat.
"That's Abe Lincoln."
They thought no more than that.

Knew that he was honest,
Guessed that he was odd,
Knew he had a cross wife
Though she was a Todd.

Knew he had three little boys
Who liked to shout and play,
Knew he had a lot of debts
It took him years to pay.

Knew his clothes and knew his house.
"That's his office, here.
Blame good lawyer, on the whole,
Though he's sort of queer.

"Sure, he went to Congress, once,
But he didn't stay.
Can't expect us all to be
Smart as Henry Clay.

"Need a man for troubled times?
Well, I guess we do.
Wonder who we'll ever find?
Yes—I wonder who."

That is how they met and talked,
Knowing and unknowing.
Lincoln was the green pine.
Lincoln kept on growing.

STEPHEN VINCENT BENÉT

 VALENTINE'S DAY

Romance

I will make you brooches and toys for your delight
Of bird-song at morning and star-shine at night.
I will make a palace fit for you and me
Of green days in forests and blue days at sea.

I will make my kitchen and you shall keep your room
Where white flows the river and bright blows the broom,
And you shall wash your linen and keep your body white
In rainfall at morning and dewfall at night.

And this shall be for music when no one else is near,
The fine song for singing, the rare song to hear!
That only I remember, that only you admire,
Of the broad road that stretches and the roadside fire.

ROBERT LOUIS STEVENSON

[37]

from *Sally in Our Alley*

Of all the girls that are so smart
   There's none like pretty Sally;
She is the darling of my heart,
   And she lives in our alley.
There is no lady in the land
   Is half so sweet as Sally;
She is the darling of my heart,
   And she lives in our alley.

Of all the days that's in the week
   I dearly love but one day—
And that's the day that comes betwixt
   A Saturday and Monday;
For then I'm dressed all in my best
   To walk abroad with Sally;
She is the darling of my heart,
   And she lives in our alley.

When Christmas comes about again,
   O, then I shall have money;
I'll hoard it up, and box it all,
   I'll give it to my honey:
I would it were ten thousand pound,
   I'd give it all to Sally;
She is the darling of my heart
   And she lives in our alley.

HENRY CAREY

Valentine Promise

The moon shall be a darkness,
    The stars give no light,
If ever I prove false
    To my heart's delight;
In the middle of the ocean
    Green grow the myrtle tree,
If ever I prove false
    To my Love that loves me.

ANONYMOUS

My Luve's Like a Red, Red Rose

O my Luve's like a red, red rose,
    That's newly sprung in June:
O my Luve's like the melodie
    That's sweetly played in tune!

As fair art thou, my bonnie lass,
    So deep in luve am I;
And I will luve thee still, my dear,
    Till a' the seas gang dry.

[39]

Till a' the seas gang dry, my dear,
   And the rocks melt wi' the sun;
I will luve thee still, my dear,
   While the sands o' life shall run.

And fare thee weel, my only Luve,
   And fare thee weel a while!
And I will come again, my Luve,
   Though it were ten thousand mile.

ROBERT BURNS

Do you love me
Or do you not?
You told me once
But I forgot.

ANONYMOUS

Good Bishop Valentine

Good Bishop Valentine
Wandered all the night
Seeking out young lovers
And urging them to write:
With bags full of sugar-plums,

Rose and violet bowers,
Hearts, doves, true-love knots,
And lace-paper flowers.

Good Bishop Valentine
By the moon's beam
Went seeking out young maidens
And urging them to dream:
With ribbons for their ringlets,
Love's silken strings,
Orange-blossom posies
And gold wedding-rings.

ELEANOR FARJEON

A Pavane for the Nursery

Now touch the air softly,
Step gently. One, two . . .
I'll love you till roses
Are robin's-egg blue;
I'll love you till gravel
Is eaten for bread,
And lemons are orange,
And lavender's red.

Now touch the air softly,
Swing gently the broom.
I'll love you till windows

Are all of a room;
And the table is laid,
And the table is bare,
And the ceiling reposes
On bottomless air.

I'll love you till Heaven
Rips the stars from his coat,
And the Moon rows away in
A glass-bottomed boat;
And Orion steps down
Like a diver below,
And Earth is ablaze,
And Ocean aglow.

So touch the air softly,
And swing the broom high,
We will dust the gray mountains,
And sweep the blue sky;
And I'll love you as long
As the furrow the plow,
As However is Ever,
And Ever is Now.

WILLIAM JAY SMITH

Valentine

I got a valentine from Timmy
                        Jimmy
                        Tillie
                        Billie
                        Nicky
                        Micky
                        Ricky
                        Dicky
                        Laura
                        Nora
                        Cora
                        Flora
                        Donnie
                        Ronnie
                        Lonnie
                        Connie
                        Eva even sent me two
                        But I didn't get *none* from you!

SHELLEY SILVERSTEIN

[43]

# WASHINGTON'S BIRTHDAY

Washington Monument by Night

1

The stone goes straight.
A lean swimmer dives into night sky,
Into half-moon mist.

2

Two trees are coal black.
This is a great white ghost between.
It is cool to look at.
Strong men, strong women, come here.

3

Eight years is a long time
To be fighting all the time.

4

The republic is a dream.
Nothing happens unless first a dream.

5

The wind bit hard at Valley Forge one Christmas.
Soldiers tied rags on their feet.
Red footprints wrote on the snow . . .
. . . and stone shoots into stars here
. . . into half-moon mist tonight.

6

Tongues wrangled dark at a man.
He buttoned his overcoat and stood alone.
In a snowstorm, red hollyberries, thoughts,
        he stood alone.

7

Women said: He is lonely
. . . fighting . . . fighting . . . eight years . . .

8

The name of an iron man goes over the world.
It takes a long time to forget an iron man.

9

.   .   .   .
.   .   .   .

CARL SANDBURG

George Washington

George Washington is tops with me,
For he cut down the cherry tree,
And freed us from the British rule;
And helped us all stay home from school.

SHELLEY SILVERSTEIN

Leetla Giorgio Washeenton

You know w'at for ees school keep out
    Dees holiday, my son?
Wal, den, I gona tal you 'bout
    Dees Giorgio Washeenton.

Wal, Giorgio was leetla keed
    Ees leeve long time ago,
An' he gon' school for learn to read
    An' write hees nam', you know.
He moocha like for gona school
    An' learn hard all day,
Because he no gat time for fool
    Weeth bada keeds an' play.

[46]

Wal, wan cold day w'en Giorgio
    Ees steell so vera small,
He start from home, but he ees no
    Show up een school at all!
O! my! hees Pop ees gatta mad
    An' so he tal hees wife:
"Som' leetla boy ees gon' feel bad
    To-day, you bat my life!"
An' den he grab a beega steeck
    An' gon' out een da snow
An' lookin' all aroun' for seek
    Da leetla Giorgio.
Ha! w'at you theenk? Firs' theeng he see
    Where leetla boy he stan',
All tangla up een cherry tree,
    Weeth hatchet een hees han'.
"Ha! w'at you do?" hees Pop he say,
    "W'at for you busta rule
An' stay away like dees for play
    Eenstead for gon' to school?"
Da boy ees say: "I no can lie,
    An' so I speaka true.
I stay away from school for try
    An' gat som' wood for you.
I theenka deesa cherry tree
    Ees gooda size for chop,
An' so I cut heem down, you see,
    For justa help my Pop."
Hees Pop he no can gatta mad,
    But looka please' an' say:
"My leetla boy, I am so glad
    You taka holiday."

Ees good for leetla boy, you see,
    For be so bright an' try
For help hees Pop; so den he be
    A granda man bimeby.
So now you gatta holiday
    An' eet ees good, you know,
For you gon' do da sama way
    Like leetla Giorgio.
Don't play so mooch, but justa stop,
    Eef you want be som' good,
An' justa help your poor old Pop
    By carry home some wood;
An' mebbe so like Giorgio
    You grow for be so great
You gona be da Presidant
    Of dese Unita State'.

                                    T. A. DALY

Young Washington

(THE EMBASSY TO THE FRENCH FORTS, 1753)

Tie the moccasin, bind the pack,
Sling your rifle across your back,
Up! and follow the mountain track,
    Tread the Indian Trail.
North and west is the road we fare
Toward the forts of the Frenchmen, where
"Peace or War!" is the word we bear,
    Life and Death in the scale.

The leaves of October are dry on the ground,
The sheaves of Virginia are gathered and bound,
Her fallows are glad with the cry of the hound,
   The partridges whirr in the fenn;
But deep are the forests and keen are the foes
Where Monongahela in wilderness flows;
We've labors and perils and torrents and snows
To conquer before we return.

   Hall and council-room, farm and chase,
Coat of scarlet and frill of lace
All are excellent things in place;
   Joy in these if ye can.
Mine be hunting-shirt, knife and gun,
Camp aglow on the sheltered run,
Friend and foe in the checkered sun;
   That's the life for a man!

ARTHUR GUITERMAN

The Birth of Saint Patrick

On the eighth day of March it was, some people say,
That Saint Pathrick at midnight he first saw the day;
While others declare, 'twas the ninth he was born,
And 'twas all a mistake, between midnight and morn;
For mistakes will occur in a hurry and shock,
And some blamed the babby—and some blamed the
    clock—
Till with all their cross-questions sure no one could know
If the child was too fast, or the clock was too slow.

Now the first faction-fight in ould Ireland, they say,
Was all on account of Saint Pathrick's birthday;
Some fought for the eighth—for the ninth more would
    die,
And who wouldn't see right, sure they blacken'd his eye!

At last, both the factions so positive grew,
That each kept a birthday, so Pat then had two,
Till Father Mulcahy, who show'd them their sins,
Said, "No one could have two birthdays, but a twins."

Says he, "Boys, don't be fightin' for eight or for nine,
Don't be always dividin'—but sometimes combine;
Combine eight with nine, and seventeen is the mark,
So let that be his birthday,"—"Amen," says the clerk.
"If he wasn't a twins, sure our history will show
That, at least, he's worth any two saints that we know!"

SAMUEL LOVER

The Wearin' of the Green

"O Paddy dear, and did ye hear the news that's goin'
    round?
The shamrock is by law forbid to grow on Irish ground!
No more Saint Patrick's Day we'll keep, his color can't
    be seen,
For there's a cruel law ag'in the Wearin' of the Green.
I met with Napper Tandy, and he took me by the hand,
And he said, 'How's poor ould Ireland, and how does
    she stand?'
'She's the most distressful country that ever yet was seen,
For they're hanging men and women there for the
    Wearin' of the Green.'

"So if the color we must wear be England's cruel red
Let it remind us of the blood that Irishmen have shed;
And pull the shamrock from your hat, and throw it on
the sod,
But never fear, 'twill take root there, though underfoot
'tis trod.
When laws can stop the blades of grass from growin' as
they grow,
And when the leaves in summer-time their color dare
not show,
Then I will change the color too I wear in my caubeen;*
But till that day, please God, I'll stick to the Wearin'
of the Green."

But if at last our color should be torn from Ireland's heart,
Her sons with shame and sorrow from the dear old isle
will part;
I've heard a whisper of a land that lies beyond the sea
Where rich and poor stand equal in the light of freedom's
day.
O Erin, must we leave you driven by a tyrant's hand?
Must we ask a mother's blessing from a strange and
distant land?
Where the cruel cross of England shall nevermore be seen
And where, please God, we'll live and die still Wearin'
of the Green.

IRISH FOLK SONG

* caubeen: hat

[52]

PRING

Song

April, April,
Laugh thy girlish laughter;
Then, the moment after,
Weep thy girlish tears!
April, that mine ears
Like a lover greetest,
If I tell thee, sweetest,
All my hopes and fears,
April, April,
Laugh thy golden laughter,
But, the moment after,
Weep thy golden tears!

WILLIAM WATSON

April

The roofs are shining from the rain,
 The sparrows twitter as they fly,
And with a windy April grace
 The little clouds go by.

Yet the back-yards are bare and brown
 With only one unchanging tree—
I could not be so sure of Spring
 Save that it sings in me.

SARA TEASDALE

Four Little Foxes

Speak gently, Spring, and make no sudden sound;
For in my windy valley, yesterday I found
New-born foxes squirming on the ground—
 Speak gently.

Walk gently, March; forbear the bitter blow;
Her feet within a trap, her blood upon the snow,
The four little foxes saw their mother go—
 Walk softly.

[54]

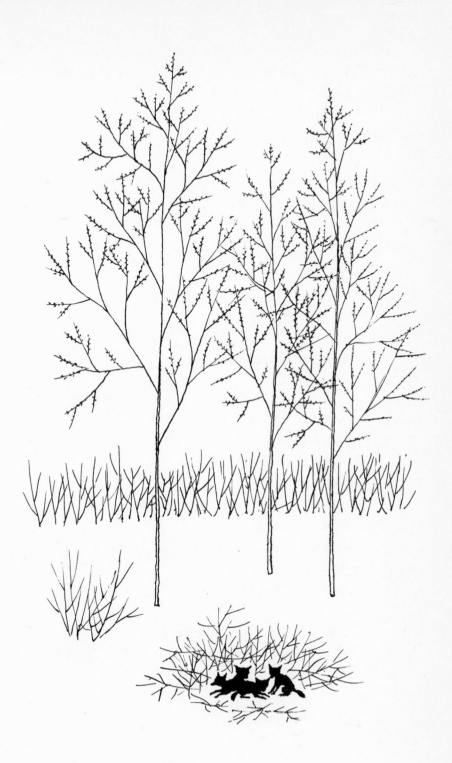

Go lightly, Spring; oh, give them no alarm;
When I covered them with boughs to shelter them from
      harm,
The thin blue foxes suckled at my arm—
    Go lightly.

Step softly, March, with your rampant hurricane;
Nuzzling one another, and whimpering with pain,
The new little foxes are shivering in the rain—
    Step softly.

LEW SARETT

I Bended unto Me

I bended unto me a bough of may,*
That I might see and smell:
It bore it in a sort of way,
It bore it very well.
But when I let it backward sway,
Then it were hard to tell
With what a toss, with what a swing,
The dainty thing
Resumed its proper level,
And sent me to the devil.
I know it did—you doubt it?
I turned, and saw them whispering about it.

T. E. BROWN

* may: hawthorn

Spring Song

I love daffodils.
I love Narcissus when he bends his head.
I can hardly keep March and spring and Sunday and
    daffodils
Out of my rhyme of song.
Do you know anything about the spring
When it comes again?
God knows about it while winter is lasting.
Flowers bring him power in the spring,
And birds bring it, and children.
He is sometimes sad and alone
Up there in the sky trying to keep his worlds happy.
I bring him songs
When he is in his sadness, and weary.
I tell him how I used to wander out
To study stars and the moon he made
And flowers in the dark of the wood.
I keep reminding him about his flowers he has forgotten,
And that snowdrops are up.
What can I say to make him listen?
"God," I say,
"Don't you care!
Nobody must be sad or sorry
In the spring-time of flowers."

HILDA CONKLING
(written when six years old)

Now that the Winter's Gone

Now that the winter's gone, the earth hath lost
Her snow-white robes, and now no more the frost
Candies the grass, or culls an icy cream
Upon the silver lake, or crystal stream;
But the warm sun thaws the benumb'd earth
And makes it tender; gives a second birth
To the dead swallow; wakes in hollow tree
The drowsy cuckoo, and the humble bee;
Now do a choir of chirping minstrels bring
In triumph to the world the youthful Spring.

THOMAS CAREW

Old Man Rain

Old Man Rain at the windowpane
Knocks and fumbles and knocks again;
His long-nailed fingers slip and strain:
Old Man Rain at the windowpane
Knocks all night but knocks in vain.
    Old Man Rain.

Old Man Rain at the windowpane
Reels and shambles along the lane;

His old gray whiskers drip and drain:
Old Man Rain with fuddled brain
Reels and staggers like one insane.
    Old Man Rain.

Old Man Rain is back again,
With old Mis' Wind at the windowpane,
Dancing there with her tattered train:
Her old shawl flaps as she whirls again
In the wildman dance and is torn in twain.
    Old Mis' Wind and Old Man Rain.

                         MADISON CAWEIN

The Ecchoing Green

The sun does arise,
And make happy the skies;
The merry bells ring
To welcome the Spring;
The skylark and thrush,
The birds of the bush,
Sing louder around
To the bells' chearful sound,
While our sports shall be seen
On the Ecchoing Green.

Old John, with white hair,
Does laugh away care,

Sitting under the oak,
Among the old folk.
They laugh at our play,
And soon they all say:
Such, such were the joys
When we all, girls & boys,
In our youth time were seen
On the Ecchoing Green.

Till the little ones, weary,
No more can be merry;
The sun does descend,
And our sports have an end.
Round the laps of their mothers
Many sisters and brothers,
Like birds in their nest,
Are ready for rest,
And sport no more seen
On the darkening Green.

WILLIAM BLAKE

from *Spring*

The Spring comes linking and jinking through the woods,
Opening wi' gentle hand the bonnie green and yellow
    buds . . .

WILLIAM MILLER

Sudden Shower

Black grows the southern sky, betokening rain,
    And humming hive-bees homeward hurry by:
They feel the change; so let us shun the grain,
    And take the broad road while our feet are dry.
Ay, there some dropples moistened on my face,
    And pattered on my hat—'tis coming nigh!
Let's look about, and find a sheltering place.
    The little things around, like you and I,
Are hurrying through the grass to shun the shower.
    Here stoops an ash-tree—hark! the wind gets high,
But never mind; this ivy, for an hour,
    Rain as it may, will keep us dryly here:
That little wren knows well his sheltering bower,
    Nor leaves his dry house though we come so near.

JOHN CLARE

Twist-rime on Spring

Upon the hills new grass is seen;
The vender's garden-sass is green.

The birds between the showers fly;
The woods are full of flowers shy.

The ornamental butterfly
Expands his wings to flutter by.

The bees, those little honey-bugs,
Are gayly dancing bunny-hugs,

While poets sing in tripping rime
That Spring's a simply ripping time!

ARTHUR GUITERMAN

Kerchoo!

I dote the baple buds are swellig—
It bust be Sprig that I ab sbellig.
Agaid, the bird is od the wig
And Dature starts her Highlad Flig.

MARGARET FISHBACK

The Brown Bear

Now the wild bees that hive in the rocks
Are winding their horns, elfin shrill,
And hark, at the pine tree the woodpecker knocks,

And the speckled grouse pipes on the hill.
Now the adder's dull brood wakes to run,
Now the sap mounts abundant and good,
And the brown bear has turned with his side to the sun
In his lair in the depth of the wood—
Old Honey-Paw wakes in the wood.

"Oh, a little more slumber," says he,
"And a little more turning to sleep,"
But he feels the spring fervor that hurries the bee
And the hunger that makes the trout leap;
So he ambles by thicket and trail,
So he noses the tender young shoots,
In the spring of year at the sign of the quail
The brown bear goes digging for roots—
For sappy and succulent roots.

Oh, as still goes the wolf on his quest
As the spotted snake glides through the rocks,
And the deer and the sheep count the lightest foot best,
And slinking and sly trots the fox.
But fleet-foot and light-foot will stay,
And fawns by their mothers will quail
At the saplings that snap and the thickets that sway
When Honey-Paw takes to the trail—
When he shuffles and grunts on the trail.

He has gathered the ground squirrel's hoard,
He has rifled the store of the bees,
He has caught the young trout at the shoals of the ford
And stripped the wild plums from the trees;

So robbing and ranging he goes,
And the right to his pillage makes good
Till he rounds out the year at the first of the snows
In his lair in the depth of the wood—
Old Honey-Paw sleeps in the wood.

MARY AUSTIN

Old Dan'l

Out of his cottage to the sun
Bent double comes old Dan'l,
His chest all over cotton wool,
His back all over flannel.

"Winter will finish him," they've said
Each winter now for ten:
But come the first warm day of Spring
Old Dan'l's out again.

L. A. G. STRONG

Upon an Easter Morning

Upon an Easter Morning,
So early in the day,
The bird raised up his whistle
To tune the night away,
The field raised up its grass-blade
Of emerald anew,
The garden raised its flower,
The river raised its dew.

Upon an Easter Morning,
So early in the day,
The organ in the chancel
Sang both grand and gay,
The people on the causey,
The cattle in the pen,

Heard the pipes of heaven
Rising up again.

The light went like a ladder
From valley-bed to sky,
The lark went like a seraph
Beyond the mortal eye.
The wind went like a spirit
To blow the dust away,
Upon an Easter Morning
So early in the day.

ELEANOR FARJEON

Alleluia! Alleluia! Let the Holy Anthem Rise

Alleluia! Alleluia! Let the holy anthem rise
    And the choirs of heaven chant it
From the temple of the skies;
    Let the mountains skip with gladness,
And the joyful valleys ring;
    For Hosanna in the highest
To our saviour and our king!

Alleluia! Alleluia! Like the sun from out the wave
    He has risen up in triumph
From the darkness of the grave;

He's the splendor of the nation
He's the lamp of endless day
    He's the very Lord of glory
Who has risen up today!

HYMN

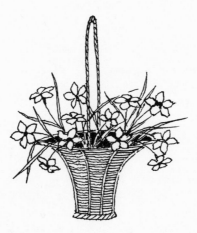

The Lent Lily

'Tis spring; come out to ramble
    The hilly brakes around,
For under thorn and bramble
    About the hollow ground
    The primroses are found.

And there's the windflower chilly
    With all the winds at play,

And there's the Lenten lily
　　That has not long to stay
　　And dies on Easter day.

And since till girls go maying
　　You find the primroses still,
And find the windflower playing
　　With every wind at will,
　　But not the daffodil.

Bring baskets now, and sally
　　Upon the spring's array,
And bear from hill and valley
　　The daffodil away
　　That dies on Easter day.

A. E. HOUSMAN

Easter

The barrier stone has rolled away,
　　And loud the angels sing;
The Christ comes forth this blessed day
　　To reign, a deathless King.
For shall we not believe He lives
　　Through such awakening?
Behold, how God each April gives
　　The miracle of Spring.

EDWIN L. SABIN

April Fools' Day

Look out! Look out! You've spilt the ink.
You're sitting in a purple puddle.
Your pants are ripped and I should think
You'd hate to have a nose so pink
And hair in such a dreadful muddle.

Look out! Behind you there's a rat.
He's hiding now behind the stool.
He's going to jump up on your hat.
Look out! Watch out! Oh dear, what's THAT!
It's only you, you April fool!

MARNIE POMEROY

[69]

There Was an Old Woman

There was an old woman, as I've heard tell,
She went to market her eggs for to sell;
She went to market all on a market day,
And she fell asleep on the king's highway.

There came by a pedlar whose name was Stout,
He cut her petticoats all round about;
He cut her petticoats up to the knees,
Which made the old woman to shiver and freeze.

When this little woman first did wake,
She began to shiver and she began to shake,
She began to wonder and she began to cry,
"Lauk a mercy on me, this is none of I!

"But if it be I, as I do hope it be,
I've a little dog at home, and he'll know me;
If it be I, he'll wag his little tail,
And if it be not I, he'll loudly bark and wail."

Home went the little woman all in the dark,
Up got the little dog, and he began to bark;
He began to bark, so she began to cry,
"Lauk a mercy on me, this is none of I!"

ANONYMOUS

Oh Did You Hear?

Oh did you hear?
The President has measles,
The Principal has just burned down the school,
Your hair is filled with jam
         and purple weasels

April Fool!

SHELLEY SILVERSTEIN

# ARBOR DAY

The Tree

I love thee when thy swelling buds appear,
And one by one their tender leaves unfold,
As if they knew that warmer suns were near,
Nor longer sought to hide from winter's cold;
And when with darker growth thy leaves are seen
To veil from view the early robin's nest,
I love to lie beneath thy waving screen,
With limbs by summer's heat and toil oppress'd;
And when the autumn winds have stript thee bare,
And round thee lies the smooth, untrodden snow,
When naught is thine that made thee once so fair,
I love to watch thy shadowy form below,
And through thy leafless arms to look above
On stars that brighter beam when most we need their
love.

JONES VERY

from *The Planting of the Apple Tree*

Come, let us plant the apple tree.
Cleave the tough greensward with the spade;
Wide let its hollow bed be made;
There gently lay the roots, and there
Sift the dark mould with kindly care,
   And press it o'er them tenderly,
As, round the sleeping infants feet,
We softly fold the cradle-sheet;
   So plant we the apple tree.

What plant we in this apple-tree?
Buds, which the breath of summer days
Shall lengthen into leafy sprays;
Boughs where the thrush, with crimson breast,
Shall haunt, and sing, and hide her nest;
   We plant, upon the sunny lea,
A shadow for the noontide hour,
A shelter from the summer shower,
   When we plant the apple-tree.

What plant we in this apple-tree?
Sweets for a hundred flowery springs
To load the May-wind's restless wings,
When, from the orchard-row, he pours
Its fragrance through our open doors;
   A world of blossoms for the bee,

Flowers for the sick girl's silent room,
For the glad infant sprigs of bloom,
    We plant with the apple-tree.

    What plant we in this apple-tree?
Fruits that shall swell in sunny June,
And redden in the August noon,
And drop, when gentle airs come by,
That fan the blue September sky,
    While children come, with cries of glee,
And seek them where the fragrant grass
Betrays their bed to those who pass,
    At the foot of the apple-tree.
                    .   .   .

    Each year shall give this apple-tree
A broader flush of roseate bloom,
A deeper maze of verdurous gloom,
And loosen, when the frost-clouds lower,
The crisp brown leaves in thicker shower.
    The years shall come and pass, but we
Shall hear no longer, where we lie,
The summer's songs, the autumn's sigh,
    In the boughs of the apple-tree.

    And time shall waste this apple-tree.
Oh, when its agèd branches throw
Thin shadows on the ground below,
Shall fraud and force and iron will
Oppress the weak and helpless still?
    What shall the tasks of mercy be,
Amid the toils, the strifes, the tears

Of those who live when length of years
　　Is wasting this little apple-tree?

　"Who planted this old apple-tree?"
The children of that distant day
Thus to some agèd man shall say;
And, gazing on its mossy stem,
The gray-haired man shall answer them:
　"A poet of the land was he,
Born in the rude but good old times;
'Tis said he made some quaint old rhymes,
　　On planting the apple tree."

WILLIAM CULLEN BRYANT

The Tree

The tree's early leaf-buds were bursting their brown.
"Shall I take them away?" said the frost sweeping down.
　"No; leave them alone
　Till the blossoms have grown,"
Prayed the tree, while he trembled from rootlet to crown.

The tree bore his blossoms, and all the birds sung.
"Shall I take them away?" said the wind, as he swung.
　"No; leave them alone
　Till the berries have grown,"
Said the tree, while his leaflets quivering hung.

[75]

The tree bore his fruit in the midsummer glow.
Said the child, "May I gather thy berries now?"
    "Yes; all thou canst see;
      Take them; all are for thee,"
Said the tree, while he bent down his laden boughs low.

BJÖRNSTJERNE BJÖRNSON

 AY DAY

Sister, Awake!

Sister, awake! close not your eyes!
  The day her light discloses,
And the bright morning doth arise
  Out of her bed of roses.

See the clear sun, the world's bright eye,
  In at our window peeping:
Lo, how he blusheth to espy
  Us idle wenches sleeping!

Therefore awake! make haste, I say,
  And let us, without staying,
All in our gowns of green so gay
  Into the Park a-maying!

ANONYMOUS

Maÿ

Come out o' door, 'tis Spring! 'tis Maÿ
The trees be green, the vields be gaÿ;
The weather's warm, the winter blast,
Wi' all his traïn o' clouds, is past;
The zun do rise while vo'k do sleep,
To teäke a higher daily zweep,
Wi' cloudless feäce a-flingèn down
His sparklèn light upon the groun'.

The aïr's a-streamèn soft,—come drow
The windor open; let it blow
In drough* the house, where vire,* an' door
A-shut, kept out the cwold avore.
Come, let the vew dull embers die,
An' come below the open sky;
An' wear your best, vor fear the groun'
In colors gäy mid sheäme your gown:
An' goo an' rig* wi' me a mile
Or two up over geäte an' stile,
Drough zunny parrocks* that do leäd,
Wi' crooked hedges, to the meäd,
Where elems high, in steätely ranks,
Do rise vrom yoller cowslip-banks,
An' birds do twitter vrom the spraÿ
O' bushes deck'd wi' snow-white maÿ;
An' gil'cups,* wi' the deäisy bed,

Be under ev'ry step you tread.
We'll wind up roun' the hill, an' look
All down the thickly-timber'd nook,
Out where the squier's house do show
His grey-walled peaks up drough the row
O' sheädy elems, where the rook
Do build her nest; an' where the brook
Do creep along the meäds, an' lie
To catch the brightness o' the sky;
An' cows, in water to theïr knees,
Do stan' a-whiskèn off the vlees.*

Mother o' blossoms, and ov all
That's feäir a-vield vrom Spring till Fall,
The gookoo* over white-weäv'd seas
Do come to zing in thy green trees,
An' buttervlees, in giddy flight,
Do gleäm the mwost by thy gaÿ light.
Oh! when, at last, my fleshly eyes
Shall shut upon the vields an' skies,
Mid zummer's zunny days be gone,
An' winter's clouds be comèn on:
Nor mid* I· draw upon the e'th,*
O' thy sweet aïr my leätest breath;
Alassen* I mid want to staÿ
Behine' for thee, O flow'ry Maÿ!

WILLIAM BARNES

* drough: through   * vlees: flies
* vire: fire   * gookoo: cuckoo
* rig: to climb playfully * mid: might
* parrocks: small fields   * e'th: earth
* gil'cups: buttercups   * Alassen: lest

Cows

Half the time they munched the grass, and all the
  time they lay
Down in the water-meadows, the lazy month of May,
      A-chewing,
      A-mooing,
   To pass the hours away.

    "Nice weather," said the brown cow.
     "Ah," said the white.
    "Grass is very tasty."
     "Grass is all right."

Half the time they munched the grass, and all the time
  they lay
Down in the water-meadows, the lazy month of May,
      A-chewing,
      A-mooing,
   To pass the hours away.

    "Rain coming," said the brown cow.
     "Ah," said the white.
    "Flies is very tiresome."
     "Flies bite."

Half the time they munched the grass, and all the time
  they lay

Down in the water-meadows, the lazy month of May,
>   A-chewing,
>   A-mooing,
> To pass the hours away.

>   "Time to go," said the brown cow.
>   "Ah," said the white.
>   "Nice chat." "Very pleasant."
>   "Night." "Night."

Half the time they munched the grass, and all the time
  they lay
Down in the water-meadows, the lazy month of May,
>   A-chewing,
>   A-mooing,
> To pass the hours away.

JAMES REEVES

May Day

>   A delicate fabric of bird song
>   Floats in the air,
>   The smell of wet wild earth
>   Is everywhere.

>   Red small leaves of the maple
>   Are clenched like a hand,
>   Like girls at their first communion
>   The pear trees stand.

Oh I must pass nothing by
  Without loving it much,
The raindrop try with my lips,
  The grass with my touch;

For how can I be sure
  I shall see again
The world on the first of May
  Shining after the rain?

SARA TEASDALE

A May Day Carol

The moon shines bright, the stars give a light,
A little before 'tis day;
Our Heavenly Father, He called to us,
And bid us awake and pray.

Awake, awake, oh pretty, pretty maid,
Out of your drowsy dream;
And step into your dairy below,
And fetch me a bowl of cream.

If not a bowl of thy sweet cream,
A cup to bring me cheer;
For the Lord knows when we shall meet again,
To go Maying another year.

I have been wandering all this night,
And some time of this day;
And now returning home again,
I've brought you a branch of May.

A branch of May I've brought you here,
And at your door I stand;
'Tis nothing but a sprout, but well budded out,
By the work of our Lord's hand.

My song is done and I must be gone,
No longer can I stay;
So it's God bless you all, both great and small,
And send you a joyful May.

OLD CAROL

Song

A sunny shaft did I behold,
    From sky to earth it slanted:
And posed therein a bird so bold—
    Sweet bird, thou wert enchanted!

He sank, he rose, he twinkled, he trolled
    Within that shaft of sunny mist;
His eyes of fire, his beak of gold,
    All else of amethyst!

[83]

And thus he sang: "Adieu! adieu!
Love's dreams prove seldom true.
The blossoms they make no delay:
The sparkling dew-drops will not stay.
  Sweet month of May,
    We must away;
      Far, far away!
        Today! today!"

SAMUEL TAYLOR COLERIDGE

OTHER'S DAY

A Mother Is a Sun

A mother is a sun. A gentle fire,
   (Sweetly luminous, softly bright)
Her warmth does not burn the living bread
She bakes within her body,

Nor blind the child she dresses
In a cloud of light
To shelter him from the storming night
Wherein owls hoot and tigers prowl.

Later she will become his moon as well,
And he himself a sun,
Sun seeking and a begetter of suns
In sun-washed days and sun-speckled nights,

In times populous with suns unmet,
Traveling among numberless crowds of suns
Known and unknown—
    (Haunted by that gentle fire).

PEGGY BENNETT

To My Mother

What matter if my words will be
As weak as weeds upon the sea,
Be sure of this, that they will show
Which way my tides of loving flow.

I watch you lift away a mask
From every drudging household task;
And leaning down as to a cup,
You smile to sip the pleasure up.
Your days are soft confiding birds
That murmur to your secret words;
Till knowledge, sunken in your eyes,
Is eloquent how you are wise.
You wear your working like a song
That only girds your spirit strong;
Till draining joy from everything
You smile to give despair a wing.

Because your living is a prayer
To keep me whole and keep me fair;

Because your gentleness is such
To heal me at the slightest touch;
Because at last I learned how true
Kindliness globes itself in you;
Because you made it clear to me
What beauty sacrifice could be;
No beauty I can ever find
Can match the beauty of your mind.

LOUIS GINSBERG

The Sick Child

Child. O mother, lay your hand on my brow!
O mother, mother, where am I now?
Why is the room so gaunt and great?
Why am I lying awake so late?

Mother. Fear not at all: the night is still.
Nothing is here that means you ill—
Nothing but lamps the whole town through,
And never a child awake but you.

Child. Mother, mother, speak low in my ear,
Some of the things are so great and near,
Some are so small and far away,
I have a fear that I cannot say.
What have I done, and what do I fear,
And why are you crying, mother dear?

[87]

Mother. Out in the city, sounds begin.
Thank the kind God, the carts come in!
An hour or two more, and God is so kind,
The day shall be blue in the window blind,
Then shall my child go sweetly asleep,
And dream of the birds and the hills of sheep.

ROBERT LOUIS STEVENSON

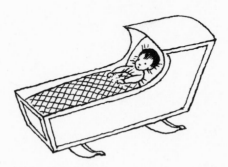

Strength and honour *are* her clothing;
　　and she shall rejoice in time to come.
She openeth her mouth with wisdom;
　　and in her tongue *is* the law of kindness.
She looketh well to the ways of her household,
　　and eateth not the bread of idleness.
Her children arise up, and call her blessed;
　　her husband *also*, and he praiseth her.
Many daughters have done virtuously,
　　but thou excellest them all.

THE BIBLE
(from Proverbs, 31)

[88]

Night and Morning

The morning sits outside afraid
Until my mother draws the shade;

Then it bursts in like a ball,
Splashing sun all up the wall.

And the evening is not night
Until she's tucked me in just right
And kissed me and turned off the light.

Oh, if my mother went away
Who would start the night and day?

DOROTHY ALDIS

MEMORIAL DAY

DECORATION DAY

Decoration Day

Sleep, comrades, sleep and rest
   On this Field of the Grounded Arms,
Where foes no more molest,
   Nor sentry's shot alarms!

Ye have slept on the ground before,
   And started to your feet
At the cannon's sudden roar,
   Or the drum's redoubling beat.

But in this Camp of Death
   No sound your slumber breaks;
Here is no fevered breath,
   No wound that bleeds and aches.

All is repose and peace,
 Untrampled lies the sod;
The shouts of battle cease,
 It is the truce of God!

Rest, comrades, rest and sleep!
 The thoughts of men shall be
As sentinels to keep
 Your rest from danger free.

Your silent tents of green
 We deck with fragrant flowers;
Yours has the suffering been,
 The memory shall be ours.

HENRY WADSWORTH LONGFELLOW

The March

I heard a voice that cried, "Make way for those who
 died!"
And all the colored crowd like ghosts at morning fled;
And down the waiting road, rank after rank there strode
In mute and measured march a hundred thousand dead.

A hundred thousand dead, with firm and noiseless tread,
All shadowy-gray yet solid, with faces gray and ghast,
And by the house they went, and all their brows were bent
Straight forward; and they passed, and passed, and passed
 and passed,

[91]

But O there came a place, and O there came a face,
That clenched my heart to see it, and sudden turned my
     way;
And in the face that turned I saw two eyes that burned,
Never-forgotten eyes, and they had things to say.

Like desolate stars they shone one moment, and were
    gone,
And I sank down and put my arms across my head,
And felt them moving past, nor looked to see the last,
In steady silent march, our hundred thousand dead.

J. C. SQUIRE

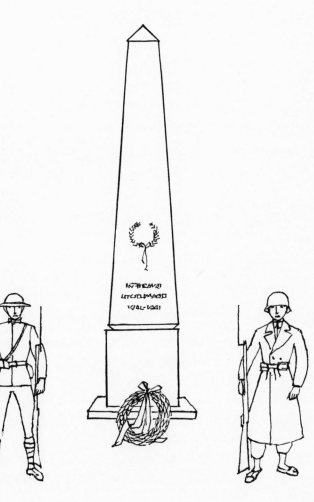

May Thirtieth
(DECORATION DAY)

Dewdrops hang from leaf and stem,
Each one glistening like a gem.
Carols echo through the air,
Overarching skies are fair.
Rose in bud and bloom of May,
All, dear child, are yours to-day.
Tenderly strew fragrant flowers,
In the shining morning hours,
Over those who, laid to rest,
Nobly gave us of their best.

Deeds of heroes theirs have been,
And through future years serene
You must keep their memory green.

ANONYMOUS

Memorial Day

A handful of old men walking down the village street
  In worn, brushed uniforms, their gray heads high;
A faded flag above them, one drum to lift their feet—
  Look again, O heart of mine, and see what passes by!

[94]

There's a vast crowd swaying, there's a wild band playing,
   The streets are full of marching men, or tramping
   cavalry.
Alive and young and straight again, they ride to greet a
   mate again—
   The gallant souls, the great souls that live eternally!

A handful of old men walking down the highways?
   Nay, we look on heroes that march among their peers,
The great, glad Companions have swung from heaven's
   byways
   And come to join their own again across the dusty
   years.

There are strong hands meeting, there are staunch hearts
   greeting—
   A crying of remembered names, of deeds that shall not
   die
A handful of old men? —Nay, my heart, look well again;
   The spirit of America today is marching by!

THEODOSIA GARRISON

LAG DAY

Brother, Lift Your Flag with Mine

Brother, sing your country's anthem,
    Shout your land's undying fame;
Light the wondrous tale of nations
    With your people's golden name.
Tell your fathers' noble story,
    Raise on high your country's sign,
Join, then, in the final glory—
    Brother, lift your flag with mine!

Hail the sun of peace new rising,
    Hold the war clouds closer furled.
Blend our banners, O my brother,
    In the rainbow of the world!
Red as blood, and blue as heaven,
    Wise as age and proud as youth,

Melt our colors, wonder-woven,
    In the great white light of truth!

Build the road of peace before us,
    Build it wide and deep and long:
Speed the slow and check the eager,
    Help the weak and curb the strong.
None shall push aside another,
    None shall let another fall:
March beside me, O my brother,
    All for one and one for all!

JOSEPHINE DASKAM BACON

Barbara Frietchie

Up from the meadows rich with corn,
Clear in the cool September morn,

The clustered spires of Frederick stand
Green-walled by the hills of Maryland.

Round about them orchards sweep,
Apple and peach tree fruited deep,

Fair as the garden of the Lord
To the eyes of the famished rebel horde,

On that pleasant morn of the early fall
When Lee marched over the mountain-wall,—

Over the mountains winding down,
Horse and foot, into Frederick town.

Forty flags with their silver stars,
Forty flags with their crimson bars,

Flapped in the morning wind: the sun
Of noon looked down, and saw not one.

Up rose old Barbara Frietchie then,
Bowed with her fourscore years and ten;

Bravest of all in Frederick town,
She took up the flag the men hauled down;

In her attic window the staff she set,
To show that one heart was loyal yet.

Up the street came the rebel tread,
Stonewall Jackson riding ahead.

Under his slouched hat left and right
He glanced: the old flag met his sight.

"Halt!"—the dust-brown ranks stood fast.
"Fire!"—out blazed the rifle-blast.

It shivered the window, pane and sash;
It rent the banner with seam and gash.

Quick, as it fell, from the broken staff
Dame Barbara snatched the silken scarf.

She leaned far out on the window-sill,
And shook it forth with a royal will.

"Shoot, if you must, this old gray head,
But spare your country's flag," she said.

A shade of sadness, a blush of shame,
Over the face of the leader came;

The nobler nature within him stirred
To life at that woman's deed and word;

"Who touches a hair of yon gray head
Dies like a dog! March on!" he said.

All day long through Frederick street
Sounded the tread of marching feet;

All day long that free flag tost
Over the heads of the rebel host.

Ever its torn folds rose and fell
On the loyal winds that loved it well;

And through the hill-gaps, sunset light
Shone over it with a warm good-night.

Barbara Frietchie's work is o'er,
And the Rebel rides on his raids no more.

Honor to her! and let a tear
Fall, for her sake, on Stonewall's bier.

Over Barbara Frietchie's grave,
Flag of Freedom and Union, wave!

Peace and order and beauty draw
Round thy symbol of light and law;

And ever the stars above look down
On thy stars below in Frederick town!

JOHN GREENLEAF WHITTIER

The Flag

One star is Minnesota
One star is South Dakota
One star is for Nebraska
One star is for Alaska
One star is for Montana
One star is Indiana
There are lots of other stars—
But I forget which ones they are

SHELLEY SILVERSTEIN

Father's Story

We put more coal on the big red fire,
And while we are waiting for dinner to cook,
Our father comes and tells us about
A story that he has read in a book.

And Charles and Will and Dick and I
And all of us but Clarence are there.
And some of us sit on Father's legs,
But one has to sit on the little red chair.

And when we are sitting very still,
He sings us a song or tells a piece;
He sings Dan Tucker Went to Town,
Or he tells us about the golden fleece.

He tells us about the golden wool,
And some of it is about a boy
Named Jason, and about a ship,
And some is about a town called Troy.

And while he is telling or singing it through,
I stand by his arm, for that is my place.
And I push my fingers into his skin
To make little dents in his big round face.

ELIZABETH MADOX ROBERTS

Father

His eyes can be quite old and stern;
But I have often watched them yearn
Over an animal in pain.
And I have seen him through the rain
Carry young lambs into the fold.
If a September night turns cold
He leaves his sleep, and in the gloom
Covers the bushes that might bloom.
I know that when his eyes grow dim
The first young bud will shout to him;
For, in the Spring I see him kneel
Upon the rigid earth and feel
With gentle hands among the leaves.
No glistening rim of frost deceives
His instinct for arbutus flowers.

He sings during his working hours
In a young voice, a rousing song
And sweeps the lagging work along.
To the delighted earth he brings
Abounding love of little things.
So, when he climbs the slope to meet
The rising sun, they kiss his feet.

MILDRED WESTON

The Secret Heart

Across the years he could recall
His father one way best of all.

In the stillest hour of night
The boy awakened to a light.

Half in dreams, he saw his sire
With his great hands full of fire.

The man had struck a match to see
If his son slept peacefully.

He held his palms each side the spark
His love had kindled in the dark.

His two hands were curved apart
In the semblance of a heart.

He wore, it seemed to his small son,
A bare heart on his hidden one,

A heart that gave out such a glow
No son awake could bear to know.

It showed a look upon his face
Too tender for the day to trace.

One instant, it lit all about,
And then the secret heart went out.

But it shone long enough for one
To know that hands held up the sun.

ROBERT P. TRISTRAM COFFIN

UMMER

Summer Song

There are white moon daisies in the mist of the meadow
    Where the flowered grass scatters its seeds like spray,
There are purple orchis by the wood-ways' shadow,
    There are pale dog-roses by the white highway;
    And the grass, the grass is tall, the grass is up for hay,
With daisies white like silver and the buttercups like
    gold,
    And it's oh! for once to play thro' the long, the lovely
    day,
To laugh before the year grows old!

There is silver moonlight on the breast of the river
    Where the willows tremble to the kiss of night,
Where the nine tall aspens in the meadow shiver,
    Shiver in the night wind that turns them white.

And the lamps, the lamps are lit, the lamps the glow-
    worms light,
Between the silver aspens and the west's last gold.
    And it's oh! to drink delight in the lovely lonely night,
To be young before the heart grows old!

E. NESBIT

The Throstle

"Summer is coming, summer is coming,
I know it, I know it, I know it.
Light again, leaf again, life again, love again,"
Yes, my wild little Poet.

Sing the new year in under the blue.
Last year you sang it as gladly.
"New, new, new, new!" Is it then *so* new
That you should carol so madly?

"Love again, song again, nest again, young again!"
Never a prophet so crazy!
And hardly a daisy as yet, little friend,
See, there is hardly a daisy.

"Here again, here, here, here happy year!"
Oh, warble unchidden, is coming, my dear,
And all the winters are hidden.

ALFRED, LORD TENNYSON

Peace and Joy

Peace and joy
And love and warmth
And happiness
Throughout the nation

Summer vacation!

SHELLEY SILVERSTEIN

Midsummer Pause

There is a moment in midsummer when the earth
pauses between flower and fruit; the hay is cut,
the oats ripen, on pasture knolls pearly everlasting
lifts its small fountains of silver and gold.

The skies are blue, the hills rest all day
like men at noon under a shady tree.
The leaves have turned dark green, they hoard
their strength, no strong wind harms them.
Boys swim under the big elm by the crick.
Locusts drone in the trees; the swallows
gather on wires, and starlings in flocks
wheel over the meadows like curving hands.

FRED LAPE

Laughing Song

When the green woods laugh with the voice of joy,
And the dimpling stream runs laughing by;
When the air does laugh with our merry wit,
And the green hill laughs with the noise of it;

When the meadows laugh with lively green,
And the grasshopper laughs in the merry scene,
When Mary and Susan and Emily
With their sweet round mouths sing "Ha, Ha, He!"

When the painted birds laugh in the shade,
Where our table with cherries and nuts is spread,
Come live and be merry, and join with me,
To sing the sweet chorus of "Ha, Ha, He!"

WILLIAM BLAKE

Poem

maggie and milly and molly and may
went down to the beach(to play one day)

and maggie discovered a shell that sang
so sweetly she couldn't remember her troubles,and

milly befriended a stranded star
whose rays five languid fingers were;

and molly was chased by a horrible thing
which raced sideways while blowing bubbles:and

may came home with a smooth round stone
as small as a world and as large as alone.

For whatever we lose(like a you or a me)
it's always ourselves we find in the sea

E. E. CUMMINGS

Midsummer Fantasy

Through the street as I trot when the weather is hot,
Then I envy the lot of a Hottentot tot,
For he lies in the shade of a glade just arrayed
In the very same costume in which he was made.
    I'd be pinched on the spot
    If I so far forgot
    As to copy the style of
    The Hottentot tot.

Oh, the Hottentot tot, though you like him or not,
In his tropical grot he can teach us a lot;
For he cares not who stares at the costume he wears,
For his neighbors are natives and tigers and bears;

And they do not care what
He is wearing. The lot
Are all dressed up the same as
The Hottentot tot.

NEWMAN LEVY

Summer Morning

I love to peep out on a summer's morn,
    Just as the scouting rabbit seeks her shed,
And the coy hare squats nestling in the corn,
    Frit* at the bow'd ear tott'ring o'er her head;
And blund'ring pheasant, that from covert springs,
    His short sleep broke by early trampling feet,
Makes one to startle with his rustling wings,
    As through the boughs he seeks more safe retreat.
The little flower, begemm'd around with drops
    That shine at sunrise like to burnish'd gold,
'Tis sweet to view: the milk-maid often stops,
    And wonders much such spangles to behold;
The hedger, too, admires them deck the thorn,
And thinks he sees no beauties like the morn.

JOHN CLARE

* frit: frightened

[111]

THE FOURTH OF JULY
INDEPENDENCE DAY

from Listen to the People: Independence Day, 1941

This is Independence Day,
Fourth of July, the day we mean to keep,
Whatever happens and whatever falls
Out of a sky grown strange;
This is firecracker day for sunburnt kids,
The day of the parade,
Slambanging down the street.
Listen to the parade!
There's J.K. Burney's float,
Red-white-and-blue crepe-paper on the wheels,
The Fire Department and the local Grange,
There are the pretty girls with their hair curled
Who represent the Thirteen Colonies,
The spirit of East Greenwich, Betsy Ross,
Democracy, or just some pretty girls.

There are the veterans and the Legion Post
(Their feet are going to hurt when they get home),
The band, the flag, the band, the usual crowd,
Good-humored, watching, hot,
Silent a second as the flag goes by,
Kidding the local cop and eating popsicles,
Jack Brown and Rosie Shapiro and Dan Shay,
Paul Bunchick and the Greek who runs the Greek's,
The black-eyed children out of Sicily,
The girls who giggle and the boys who push,
All of them there and all of them a nation.
And, afterwards,
There'll be ice-cream and fireworks and a speech
By Somebody the Honorable Who,
The lovers will pair off in the kind dark
And Tessie Jones, our honor-graduate,
Will read the Declaration.
That's how it is. It's always been that way.
That's our Fourth of July, through war and peace,
That's our Fourth of July.

STEPHEN VINCENT BENÉT

Grandfather Watts's Private Fourth

Grandfather Watts used to tell us boys
That a Fourth wa'n't a Fourth without any noise.
He would say, with a thump of his hickory stick,
That it made an American right down *sick*

To see his sons on the Nation's Day
Sit round, in a sort of a listless way,
With no oration and no train-band,
No fire-work show and no root-beer stand;
While his grandsons, before they were out of bibs,
Were ashamed—Great Scott!—to fire off squibs.

And so, each Independence morn,
Grandfather Watts took his powder-horn,
And the flint-lock shot-gun *his* father had
When he fought under Schuyler, a country lad;
And Grandfather Watts would start and tramp
Ten miles to the woods at Beaver Camp;
For Grandfather Watts used to say—and scowl—
That a decent chipmunk, or woodchuck, or owl
Was better company, friendly or shy,
Than folks who didn't keep Fourth of July.
And so he would pull his hat down on his brow,
And march for the woods, sou'-east by sou'.

But once—ah, long, long years ago,—
For Grandfather's gone where good men go,—
One hot, hot Fourth, by ways of our own
(Such short-cuts as boys have always known),
We hurried, and followed the dear old man
Beyond where the wilderness began—
To the deep black woods at the foot of the Hump;
And there was a clearing—and a stump.
A stump in the heart of a great wide wood,
And there on that stump our Grandfather stood,
Talking and shouting out there in the sun,

And firing that funny old flint-lock gun
Once in a minute—his head all bare—
Having his Fourth of July out there:
The Fourth of July that he used to know,
Back in eighteen-and-twenty or so!

First, with his face to the heavens blue,
He read the "Declaration" through:
And then, with gestures to left and right,
He made an oration erudite,
Full of words six syllables long—
And then our Grandfather burst into song!
And, scaring the squirrels in the trees,
Gave "Hail, Columbia!" to the breeze.

And I tell you the old man never heard
When we joined in the chorus, word for word!
But he sang out strong to the bright blue sky;
And if voices joined in his Fourth of July,
He heard them as echoes from days gone by.

And when he had done, we all slipped back,
As still as we came, on our twisting track,
While words more clear than the flint-lock shots
Rang in our ears.
   And Grandfather Watts?

He shouldered the gun his father bore,
And marched off home, nor'-west by nor'.

H. C. BUNNER

If I Had a Firecracker

If I had a firecracker
Twelve feet high,
And taller than fifteen men,
I'd set it off on the Fourth of July
And blow Lucille twelve miles high
So she wouldn't come down till *next* July.
And then I'd do it again.

SHELLEY SILVERSTEIN

Fireworks

They rise like sudden fiery flowers
   ·That burst upon the night,
Then fall to earth in burning showers
   Of crimson, blue, and white.

Like buds too wonderful to name,
   Each miracle unfolds,
And catherine-wheels begin to flame
   Like whirling· marigolds.

Rockets and roman candles make
   An orchard of the sky,
Whence magic trees their petals shake
   Upon each gazing eye.

JAMES REEVES

LABOR DAY

I Hear America Singing

I hear America singing, the varied carols I hear,
Those of mechanics, each one singing his as it should be
    blithe and strong,
The carpenter singing as he measures his plank or beam,
The mason singing his as he makes ready for work, or
    leaves off work,
The boatman singing what belongs to him in his boat,
    the deckhand singing on the steamboat deck,
The shoemaker singing as he sits on his bench,
    the hatter singing as he stands,
The wood-cutter's song, the ploughboy's on his way in
    the morning, or at noon intermission or at sundown,
The delicious singing of the mother, or of the young wife
    at work, or of the girl sewing or washing,

Each singing what belongs to him or her and to none else,
The day what belongs to the day—at night
    the party of young fellows, robust, friendly,
Singing with open mouths their strong melodious songs.

WALT WHITMAN

There you sit
On your lawn
My happy, sleepy neighbor;
Aren't you glad on Labor Day
There isn't any labor?

SHELLEY SILVERSTEIN

Labor Day

The working people long ago
Laid down pen and tool and hoe
To celebrate their flourishing trades
On a day with meetings and parades.
Now for no purpose, and free as air
We have the holiday once a year.
No one was born we must remember—
It's just a time to enjoy September.

No country was found, no battle was won—
It's just all day for a stroll in the sun
Through goldenrod and silverrod,
Hailing the sunflower heads that nod.
Through golden aster and silver grass,
Whistling at yellow birds that pass.
Counting the clouds that brightly gleam
Like thistledown drifting along the stream.
Following butterflies gilt and white
Over shining hay till the moon grows light.
To see such silver and gold on things
Makes us all richer than queens and kings.

MARNIE POMEROY

Work

No man is born into the world whose work
Is not born with him; there is always work
And tools to work withal, for those who will;
And blessed are the horny hands of toil;
   The busy world shoves angrily aside
The man who stands with arms akimbo set,
Until occasion tells him what to do;
And he who waits to have his task marked out,
Shall die and leaves his errand unfulfilled.

JAMES RUSSELL LOWELL

A Child's Thought of Harvest

Out in the fields which were green last May,
But are rough and stubbled and brown to-day,
They are stacking the sheaves of the yellow wheat,
And raking the aftermath dry and sweet,
The barley and oats and golden rye
Are safely stored in the granary;
Where the pumpkins border the tall corn rows,
The busy reaper comes and goes;
And only the apples set so thick
On the orchard boughs are left to pick.

What a little time it seems since May—
Not very much longer than yesterday!
Yet all this growing, which now is done
And finished, was scarcely then begun.

The nodding wheat and high, strong screen
Of corn were but little points of green.
The apple blossoms were pink and sweet,
But no one could gather them to eat;
And all this food for hungry men
Was but buds or seeds just planted then.

SUSAN COOLIDGE

A Vagabond Song

There is something in the autumn that is native to my
     blood—
Touch of manner, hint of mood;
And my heart is like a rhyme,
With the yellow and the purple and the crimson keeping
     time.

The scarlet of the maples can shake me like a cry
Of bugles going by.
And my lonely spirit thrills
To see the frosty asters like a smoke upon the hills.

There is something in October sets the gypsy blood astir;
We must rise and follow her,
When from every hill of flame
She calls and calls each vagabond by name.

BLISS CARMAN

October's Song

The forest's afire!
The forest's afire!
The maple is burning,
The sycamore's turning,
The beech is alight!
Make a pyre! make a pyre!
Bring the oak to the fire!
The forest is glowing!
The greenleaf is flowing
In flame out of sight!

ELEANOR FARJEON

An Autumnal Evening

Deep black against the dying glow
The tall elms stand; the rooks are still;
No windbreath makes the faintest thrill
Amongst the leaves; the fields below
Are vague and dim in twilight shades—
Only the bats wheel in their raids
On the grey flies, and silently
Great dusky moths go flitting by.

WILLIAM SHARP

God's World

O World, I cannot hold thee close enough!
    Thy winds, thy wide grey skies!
    Thy mists, that roll and rise!
Thy woods, this autumn day, that ache and sag
And all but cry with colour! That gaunt crag
To crush! To lift the lean of that black bluff!
World, World, I cannot get thee close enough!

Long have I known a glory in it all,
    But never knew I this:
    Here such a passion is
As stretcheth me apart,—Lord, I do fear
Thou'st made the world too beautiful this year;
My soul is all but out of me,—let fall
No burning leaf; prithee, let no bird call.

EDNA ST. VINCENT MILLAY

Something Told the Wild Geese

Something told the wild geese
    It was time to go.
Though the fields lay golden
    Something whispered,—"Snow."

Leaves were green and stirring,
    Berries luster-glossed,
But beneath warm feathers
    Something cautioned,—"Frost."
All the sagging orchards
    Steamed with amber spice,
But each wild breast stiffened
    At remembered ice.
Something told the wild geese
    It was time to fly,—
Summer sun was on their wings,
    Winter in their cry.

RACHEL FIELD

Late October

I found ten kinds of wild flowers growing
On a steely day that looked like snowing:
Queen Anne's lace, and blue heal-all,
A buttercup, straggling, grown too tall,
A rusty aster, a chicory flower—
Ten I found in half an hour.
The air was blurred with dry leaves flying,
Gold and scarlet, gaily dying.
A squirrel ran off with a nut in his mouth,
And always, always, flying south,
Twittering, the birds went by
Flickering sharp against the sky,

Some in great bows, some in wedges,
Some in bands with wavering edges;
Flocks and flocks were flying over
With the north wind for their drover.
"Flowers," I said, "you'd better go,
Surely it's coming on for snow,"—
They did not heed me, nor heed the birds,
Twittering thin, far-fallen words—
The others thought of tomorrow, but they
Only remembered yesterday.

SARA TEASDALE

The Last Flower

"It seems a shame,"
Said the wood mouse.

The hedgehog nodded,
"So it goes."
He looked at the sky and added,
"One never knows."

"Will she wake?"
The wood mouse whispered.
"Will she know her name?"

The two were silent for a moment . . .

Winter came.

JOHN TRAVERS MOORE

October's Bright Blue Weather

O sun and skies and clouds of June,
    And flowers of June together,
Ye cannot rival for one hour
    October's bright blue weather,

When loud the bumble-bee makes haste,
    Belated, thriftless vagrant,
And goldenrod is dying fast,
    And lanes with grapes are fragrant;

When gentians roll their fingers tight
    To save them for the morning,
And chestnuts fall from satin burrs
    Without a sound of warning;

When on the ground red apples lie
    In piles like jewels shining,
And redder still on old stone walls
    Are leaves of woodbine twining;

When all the lovely wayside things
    Their white-winged seeds are sowing,
And in the fields, still green and fair,
    Late aftermaths are growing;

When springs run low, and on the brooks,
  In idle golden freighting,
Bright leaves sink noiseless in the hush
  Of woods, for winter waiting;

When comrades seek sweet country haunts,
  By twos and twos together,
And count like misers hour by hour,
  October's bright blue weather.

O suns and skies and flowers of June,
  Count all your boasts together,
Love loveth best of all the year
  October's bright blue weather.

HELEN HUNT JACKSON

Autumn

Autumn's good, a cosy season;
Then there's work for man and woman,
While each day the sunlight dwindles
Speckled fawn through reddening bracken
  Scatter from the herd.

Stags leap up from sandy hollows
Answering the hind's deep bellow,
Acorns drop in peaceful woodlands,

[129]

Corn stands up in golden plenty
 Over the brown world.

Even the spiky thorn-bush growing
By the old deserted fortress
Staggers with its weight of berries,
Hazel nuts thud in the forest
 From the wearied boughs.

Translated from the Irish by FRANK O'CONNOR

Columbus

How in Heaven's name did Columbus get over
　　Is a pure wonder to me, I protest;
Cabot, and Raleigh too, that well-read rover,
　　Frobisher, Dampier, Drake, and the rest.
　　　　Bad enough all the same,
　　　　For them that after came,
　　　　But, in great Heaven's name,
　　　　How *he* should ever think
　　　　That on the other brink
Of this wild waste, terra firma should be,
Is a pure wonder, I must say, to me.

How a man ever should hope to get thither,
　　E'en if he knew that there was another side;
But to suppose he should come any whither,

Sailing straight on into chaos untried,—
　　In spite of the motion
　　Across the whole ocean,
　　To stick to the notion
　　That in some nook or bend
　　Of a sea without end
He should find North and South America,
Was a pure madness, indeed I must say.

What if wise men had, as far back as Ptolemy,
　　Judged that the earth like an orange was round,
None of them ever said, "Come along, follow me,
　　Sail to the West and the East will be found."
　　Many a day before
　　Even they'd come ashore,
　　Sadder and wiser men,
　　They'd have turned back again;
And that *he* did not, but did cross the sea,
Is a pure wonder, I must say, to me.

ARTHUR HUGH CLOUGH

The Discovery

There was an Indian, who had known no change,
Who strayed content along a sunlit beach
Gathering shells. He heard a sudden strange
Commingled noise; looked up; and gasped for speech.

For in the bay, where nothing was before,
Moved on the sea, by magic, huge canoes,
With bellying cloths on poles, and not one oar
And fluttering colored signs and clambering crews.

And he, in fear, this naked man alone,
His fallen hands forgetting all their shells,
His lips gone pale, knelt low behind a stone,
And stared, and saw, and did not understand,
Columbus's doom-burdened caravels
Slant to the shore, and all their seamen land.

J. C. SQUIRE

The Great Discovery
(12 OCTOBER, COLUMBUS DAY)

Christofero had a mind
Facts were powerless to bind.

He declared that he had seen
Mermaids sporting on the green,

And the world, he used to swear,
Was not an orange, but a pear.

Little wonder then that he,
Blown across the unknown sea

On the quest of far Cathay,
Lit upon the U.S.A.,

And while seeking for the Khan
Met his first Red Indian.

ELEANOR FARJEON

HALLOWEEN

Hallowe'en

Tonight is the night
When dead leaves fly
Like witches on switches
Across the sky,
When elf and sprite
Flit through the night
On a moony sheen.

Tonight is the night
When leaves make a sound
Like a gnome in his home
Under the ground,
When spooks and trolls
Creep out of holes
Mossy and green.

Tonight is the night
When pumpkins stare
Through sheaves and leaves
Everywhere,
When ghoul and ghost
And goblin host
Dance round their queen.
It's Hallowe'en!

HARRY BEHN

On Halloween

On Halloween I'll go to town
And wear my trousers upside down,
And wear my shoes turned inside out
And wear a wig of sauerkraut.

SHELLEY SILVERSTEIN

The Hag

The Hag is astride,
    This night for to ride;
The Devil and she together:
    Through thick and through thin,
    Now out, and then in,
Though ne'er so foul be the weather.

    A Thorn or a Burr
    She takes for a Spur:
With a lash of a Bramble she rides now,
    Through Brakes and through Briars,
    O'er Ditches, and Mires,
She follows the Spirit that guides now.

No Beast, for his food,
  Dares now range the wood;
But hush't in his lair he lies lurking:
  While mischiefs, by these,
  On Land and on Seas,
At noon of Night are a working.

  The storm will arise,
  And trouble the skies;
This night, and more for the wonder,
  The ghost from the Tomb
  Affrighted shall come,
Called out by the clap of the Thunder.

ROBERT HERRICK

Halloween

Who raps at my window?
Who in a white sheet
Runs across the midnight lawn
Without the sound of feet?

What moon grows in the East
So huge and dusky red?
Who howls from the chill within the hill
Where the farmer's hound lies dead?

The dry leaves twist and rattle
Alive in an evil spell.

Down by the pond the man who drowned
Tolls a wavering bell.

The wind has hardly wakened,
Yet flapping through the air
Fly shapes with wings and bony things
And forms with jagged hair.

Who blows at my candle?
Whose fiery grin and eyes
Behind me pass in the looking glass
And make my gooseflesh rise?

Who moved in that shadow?
Who rustles past unseen?
With the dark so deep I dare not sleep
All night on Halloween.

MARNIE POMEROY

Hallowe'en Indignation Meeting

A sulky witch and a surly cat
And a scowly owl and a skeleton sat
With a grouchy ghost and a waspish bat,
And angrily snarled and chewed the fat.

It seems they were all upset and riled
That they couldn't frighten the Modern Child,

Who was much too knowing and much too wild
And considered Hallowe'en spooks too mild.

Said the witch, "They call this the *human* race,
Yet the kiddies inhabit Outer Space;
They bob for comets, and eat ice cream
From flying saucers, to get up steam!"

"I'm a shade of my former self," said the skeleton.
"I shiver and shake like so much gelatine,
Indeed I'm a pitiful sight to see—
I'm scareder of *kids* than they are of *me!*"

MARGARET FISHBACK

Ghoulies and Ghosties

From ghoulies and ghosties,
Long-leggity beasties,
And things that go *bump* in the night,
Good Lord deliver us.

OLD SPELL

BOOK WEEK

A Book

I'm a strange contradiction; I'm new and I'm old,
I'm often in tatters and oft deck'd in gold:
Though I never could read, yet letter'd I'm found;
Though blind, I enlighten; though loose, I am bound—
I am always in black, and I'm always in white;
I am grave and I'm gay, I am heavy and light.
In form too I differ—I'm thick and I'm thin,
I've no flesh, and no bones, yet I'm cover'd with skin;
I've more points than the compass, more stops than the
     flute—
I sing without voice, without speaking confute;
I'm English, I'm German, I'm French and I'm Dutch;
Some love me too fondly; some slight me too much;
I often die soon, though sometimes live ages,
And no monarch alive has so many pages.

HANNAH MORE

O for a Booke

O for a Booke and a shadie nooke,
   eyther in-a-doore or out;
With the grene leaves whispering overhede,
   or the Streete cryes all about.
Where I maie Reade all at my ease,
   both of the Newe and Olde;
For a jollie goode Booke whereon to looke,
   is better to me than Golde.

OLD ENGLISH

If someone asks you
What you know,
What you can tell them
About such and so
   And you answer
   I don't know;

If someone asks you
Do you know much,
What you can tell them
About so and such

And you answer
Not *too* much.

I'd say
  That either
    Mr. Someone
      Or yourself
Should take a book down from the shelf.

MITCHELL DONIAN

ETERANS' DAY
ARMISTICE DAY

Everyone Sang

Everyone suddenly burst out singing;
And I was filled with such delight
As prisoned birds must find in freedom,
Winging wildly across the white
Orchards and dark-green fields; on—on—and out of
 sight.

Everyone's voice was suddenly lifted;
And beauty came like the setting sun:
My heart was shaken with tears; and horror
Drifted away . . . Oh, but Everyone
Was a bird; and the song was wordless; the singing will
 never be done.

SIEGFRIED SASSOON

[144]

When Johnny Comes Marching Home

When Johnny comes marching home again, hurrah!
    hurrah!
We'll give him a hearty welcome, then, hurrah! hurrah!
The men will cheer, the boys will shout,
The ladies they will all turn out;
And we'll all feel gay when Johnny comes marching
    home.

The old church bell will peal with joy, hurrah! hurrah!
To welcome home our darling boy, hurrah! hurrah!
The village lads and lassies say,
With roses they will strew the way;
And we'll all feel gay when Johnny comes marching
    home.

Get ready for the Jubilee, hurrah! hurrah!
We'll give the hero three times three, hurrah! hurrah!
The laurel wreath is ready now,
To place upon his loyal brow;
And we'll all feel gay when Johnny comes marching
    home.

PATRICK SARSFIELD GILMORE

THANKSGIVING

Thanksgiving Wishes

I wish you all that pen and ink
    Could write, and then some more!
I hope you cannot even think
    Of half you're thankful for.

I hope your table holds a wealth
    Of prime Thanksgiving fare,
And Love and Peace and Joy and Health
    Will all be seated there.

I trust your guests will all be bright,
    But none of them too wise,
And each will bring an appetite
    For mince or pumpkin pies.

I hope the fowls will all be fat,
    The cider sweet to quaff,
And when you snap a Wishbone, that
    You'll win the larger half!

ARTHUR GUITERMAN

When Father Carves the Duck

We all look on with anxious eyes
    When father carves the duck,
And mother almost always sighs
    When father carves the duck;
Then all of us prepare to rise,
And hold our bibs before our eyes,
And be prepared for some surprise,
    When father carves the duck.

He braces up and grabs a fork
    Whene'er he carves a duck,
And won't allow a soul to talk
    Until he's carved the duck,
The fork is jabbed into the sides,
Across the breast the knife he slides,
While every careful person hides
    From flying chips of duck.

The platter's always sure to slip
    When father carves a duck,

And how it makes the dishes skip!
    Potatoes fly amuck!
The squash and cabbage leap in space,
We get some gravy in our face,
And father mutters Hindoo grace
    Whene'er he carves a duck.

We then have learned to walk around
    The dining room and pluck
From off the window sills and walls
    Our share of father's duck.
While father growls and blows and jaws
And swears the knife was full of flaws,
And mother laughs at him because
    He couldn't carve a duck.

E. V. WRIGHT

The Pumpkin

Ah! on Thanksgiving Day, when from East and from
    West,
From North and from South come the pilgrim and guest,
When the gray-haired New Englander sees round his
    board
The old broken links of affection restored,
When the care-wearied man seeks his mother once more,
And the worn matron smiles where the girl smiled before,
What moistens the lip and what brightens the eye?
What calls back the past, like the rich Pumpkin pie?

Oh—fruit loved of boyhood—the old days recalling,
When wood-grapes were purpling and brown nuts were
    falling!
When wild, ugly faces we carved in its skin,
Glaring out through the dark with a candle within!
When we laughed round the corn-heap, with hearts all
    in tune,
Our chair a broad pumpkin,—our lantern the moon,
Telling tales of a fairy who travelled like steam,
In a pumpkin-shell coach, with two rats for her team!

JOHN GREENLEAF WHITTIER

INTER

Signs of Winter

The cat runs races with her tail. The dog
Leaps o'er the orchard hedge and knarls* the grass.
The swine run round and grunt and play with straw,
Snatching out hasty mouthfuls from the stack.
Sudden upon the elm-tree tops the crow
Unceremonious visit pays and croaks,
Then swops away. From mossy barn the owl
Bobs hasty out—wheels round and, scared as soon,
As hastily retires. The ducks grow wild
And from the muddy pond fly up and wheel
And circle round the village and soon, tired,
Plunge in the pond again. The maids in haste
Snatch from the orchard hedge the mizzled* clothes
And laughing hurry in to keep them dry.

JOHN CLARE

* knarls: gnaws; nibbles
* mizzled: misted over

Winter Is Icumen in

Winter is icumen in,
    Loud sing kerchoo.
Bloweth wind and spreadeth germ,
    Flieth hat from head askew—
    Sing kerchoo!

Winter is icumen in,
    Loud sing kerchoo.
Breaketh back with pushing snow,
    Freezeth nose while lips go blue—
    Snort kerchoo!

BRADFORD SMITH

The Pine Bough

I saw a thing, and stopped to wonder—
For who had set the moment when
The pine bough should dip out from under
The white oppressor's arm of snow,
And upward fling itself, as though
Attracted to a blue May heaven?

RICHARD ALDRIDGE

Winter

Then comes the Winter, like a hale old man
Wrapped in his cloak with frosty locks and beard.
Winter is the time for clear cold starlight nights,
And driving snows, and frozen roads and rivers,
For crowding round the blazing Christmas fire,
For telling tales that make the blood run cold,
For sipping elder-wine and cracking filberts,
For friendships, chilblains, fun, roast beef, mince pies,
And shivering fits on jumping into bed:
And thus the year goes round, and round, and round.

JAMES HURNARD

Old Winter

Old Winter sad, in snowy clad,
    Is making a doleful din;
But let him howl, till he crack his jowl,
    We will not let him in.

Aye, let him lift from the billowy drift
    His hoary haggard form,
And scowling stand, with his wrinkled hand
    Outstretching to the storm.

And let his weird and sleety beard
  Stream loose upon the blast,
And, rustling, chime to the tinkling rime
  From his bald head falling fast.

Let his baleful breath shed blight and death
  On herb and flower and tree;
And brooks and ponds in crystal bonds
  Bind fast, but what care we?

Let him push at the door,—in the chimney roar,
  And rattle the window pane;
Let him in at us spy with his icicle eye,
  But he shall not entrance gain.

Let his gnaw, forsooth, with his freezing tooth,
  On our roof-tiles, till he tire;
But we care not a whit, as we jovial sit
  Before our blazing fire.

THOMAS NOËL

from *Winter*

When gadding snow makes hillsides white,
  And icicles form more and more;
When niggard Frost stands all the night,
  And taps at snoring Gaffer's door;
When watch-dogs bay the vagrant wind,

And shiv'ring kine herd close in shed;
When kitchens chill, and maids unkind,
　　Send rustic suitors home to bed—
　　　　Then do I say the winter cold,
　　　　It seems to me, is much too bold.

When winking sparks run up the stalk,
　　And faggots blaze within the grate,
And, by the ingle-cheek, I talk
　　With shadows from the realm of fate;
When authors old, yet ever young,
　　Look down upon me from the walls,
And songs by spirit-lips are sung
　　To pleasant tunes and madrigals,—
　　　　Then do I say the winter cold
　　　　Brings back to me the joys of old.

When morn is bleak, and sunshine cool,
　　And trav'llers' beards with rime are grey;
When frost-nipt urchins weep in school,
　　And sleighs creak o'er the drifted way;
When smoke goes quick from chimney-top,
　　And mist flies through the open hatch;
When snow-flecks to the window hop,
　　And children's tongues cling to the latch,—
　　　　Then do I sigh for summer wind,
　　　　And wish the winter less unkind.

When merry bells a-jingling go,
　　And prancing horses beat the ground;
When youthful hearts are all aglow,
　　And youthful gladness rings around;

When gallants praise, and maidens blush
    To hear their charms so loudly told,
Whilst echoing vale and echoing bush
    Halloo their laughter, fold on fold,—
        Then do I think the winter meet,
        For gallants free and maidens sweet.

But, when the winter chills my friend,
    And steals the heart-fire from his breast;
Or woos the ruffian wind to send
    One pang to rob him of his rest—
All gainless grows the Christmas cheer,
    And gloomy seems the new year's light,
For joy but lives when friends are near,
    And dies when they do quit the sight.—
        Then, winter, do I cry, "Thy greed
        Is great, ay, thou art cold indeed!"

CHARLES MAIR

January

A snow may come as quietly
as cats can walk across a floor.
It hangs its curtains in the air,
and piles its weight against the door.
It fills old nests with whiter down

than any swan has ever known,
and then, as silent as it came,
you find the pale snow bird has flown.

But snow can come quite otherwise,
with windy uproar and commotion,
with shaken trees and banging blinds,
still salty from the touch of ocean.
Such storms will wrestle with strong boys,
and set the girls' skirts wildly blowing,
until it throws its cap in air
and shouts, "Well, goodbye now! I'm going!"

ELIZABETH COATSWORTH

When Icicles Hang by the Wall

When icicles hang by the wall,
  And Dick the shepherd blows his nail,
And Tom bears logs into the hall,
  And milk comes frozen home in pail,
When blood is nipp'd and ways be foul,
Then nightly sings the staring owl—
      To-who;
Tu-whit, to-who, a merry note,
While greasy Joan doth keel the pot.

When all aloud the wind doth blow,
  And coughing drowns the parson's saw,
And birds sit brooding in the snow,

And Marion's nose looks red and raw,
When roasted crabs hiss in the bowl,
Then nightly sings the staring owl—
            To-who;
Tu-whit, to-who, a merry note,
While greasy Joan doth keel the pot.

WILLIAM SHAKESPEARE
(from Love's Labour's Lost, Act V, Scene II)

from *The First Snow-fall*

The snow had begun in the gloaming,
    And busily all the night
Had been heaping field and highway
    With a silence deep and white.

Every pine and fir and hemlock
    Wore ermine too dear for an earl,
And the poorest twig on the elm-tree
    Was ridged inch deep with pearl.

From sheds new-roofed with carrara
    Came Chanticleer's muffled crow,
The stiff rails softened to swan's-down,
    And still fluttered down the snow.

I stood and watched by the window
    The noiseless work of the sky,

And the sudden flurries of snow-birds,
Like brown leaves whirling by.

JAMES RUSSELL LOWELL

White Fields

(1)

In the winter time we go
Walking in the fields of snow;

Where there is no grass at all;
Where the top of every wall,

Every fence and every tree,
Is as white as white can be.

(2)

Pointing out the way we came,
—Every one of them the same—

All across the fields there be
Prints in silver filigree;

And our mothers always know,
By our footprints in the snow,

Where it is the children go.

JAMES STEPHENS

Up in the Morning Early

Cauld blaws the wind frae east to west,
   The drift is driving sairly;
Sae loud and shill's I hear the blast,
   I'm sure it's winter fairly.

"Up in the morning's no for me,
   Up in the morning early;
When a' the hills are cover'd wi' snaw,
   I'm sure it is winter fairly."

The birds sit chittering in the thorn,
   A' day they fare but sparely;
And lang's the night frae e'en to morn,
   I'm sure it's winter fairly.

ROBERT BURNS

Stopping by Woods on a Snowy Evening

Whose woods these are I think I know.
His house is in the village though;
He will not see me stopping here
To watch his woods fill up with snow.

[160]

My little horse must think it queer
To stop without a farmhouse near
Between the woods and frozen lake
The darkest evening of the year.

He gives his harness bells a shake
To ask if there is some mistake.
The only other sound's the sweep
Of easy wind and downy flake.

The woods are lovely, dark and deep.
But I have promises to keep,
And miles to go before I sleep,
And miles to go before I sleep.

ROBERT FROST

Triolet on a Dark Day

It's a dark and dreary season—
    Christmas trees are in the gutter.
That's the fundamental reason
It's a dark and dreary season.
Though I slip my skates or skis on,
    Still I scowl and grimly mutter,
"It's a dark and dreary season—
    Christmas trees are in the gutter."

MARGARET FISHBACK

CHRISTMAS

I Heard the Bells on Christmas Day

I heard the bells on Christmas day
Their old, familiar carols play,
And wild and sweet the words repeat
   Of peace on earth, good-will to men.

I thought how, as the day had come,
The belfries of all Christendom
Had rolled along the unbroken song
   Of peace on earth, good-will to men.

And in despair I bowed my head:
"There is no peace on earth," I said,
"For hate is strong, and mocks the song,
   Of peace on earth, good-will to men."

Then pealed the bells more loud and deep:
"God is not dead, nor doth he sleep;
The wrong shall fail, the right prevail,
   With peace on earth, good-will to men."

Till, ringing, singing on its way,
The world revolved from night to day,
A voice, a chime, a chant sublime,
   Of peace on earth, good-will to men!

               HENRY WADSWORTH LONGFELLOW

Chanson Innocente

little tree
little silent Christmas tree
you are so little
you are more like a flower

who found you in the green forest
and were you sorry to come away?
see   i will comfort you
because you smell so sweetly

i will kiss your cool bark
and hug you safe and tight
just as your mother would,
only don't be afraid

look   the spangles
that sleep all the year in a dark box
dreaming of being taken out and allowed to shine,
the balls the chains red and gold the fluffy threads,

put up your little arms
and i'll give them all to you to hold
every finger shall have its ring
and there won't be a single place dark or unhappy

then when you're quite dressed
you'll stand in the window for everyone to see
and how they'll stare!
oh but you'll be very proud

and my little sister and i will take hands
and looking up at our beautiful tree
we'll dance and sing
"Noel Noel"

E. E. CUMMINGS

Simple Sam

Said Simple Sam: "Does Christmas come
    In April or December,
In winter, spring or harvest time?
    I really can't remember."

LEROY F. JACKSON

Sweet Was the Song

Sweet was the song the Virgin sung,
When she to Bethlehem was come,
And was delivered of her Son,
That blessed JESUS hath to name,
   Lullaby,
Lullaby sweet Babe quoth she,
My Son, and eke a Saviour borne,
Who hath vouchsafed from on high,
To visit us that were forlorne,
   Lulla, Lulla,
Lullaby sweet Babe sang she,
And sweetly rockt him, rockt him, rockt him,
And sweetly rockt him on her knee.

ANONYMOUS

Christmas Song

Above the wary waiting world,
Asleep in chill despair,
There breaks a sound of joyous bells
Upon the frosted air.
And o'er the humblest rooftree, lo,
A star is dancing on the snow.

What makes the yellow star to dance
Upon the brink of night?
What makes the breaking dawn to glow
So magically bright,—
And all the earth to be renewed
With infinite beatitude?

The singing bells, the throbbing star,
The sunbeams on the snow,
And the awakening heart that leaps
New ecstasy to know,—
They all are dancing in the morn
Because a little child is born.

BLISS CARMAN

Mrs. Santa Claus' Christmas Present

At the top of the world, where fields of snow
Stretch out whichever way you go,
Where the North Star burns without a sound
And the North Pole turns the world around,

And shooting stars are rimmed with ice
And polar bears think cold is nice,
There Santa Claus and his gentle wife
Have their home and make their life.

.   .   .

Every morning—while Santa's shop
Echoes with sounds of drum and top,
And hammer blows on wood and tin,
And other kinds of deafening din—

Out in the stable, warm and dry,
The reindeer wait, as the year goes by,
For the morning sound across the floor
Of Mrs. Santa Claus at the door!

For she is the lady tall and fair,
With a quiet smile and a loving air,
Who gets the reindeer ready to ride
Across the world at Christmastide.

She shines their antlers and curries their coats,
And brings them buckets of powdered oats,
And feeds them grass (chopped fine as silk)
And foaming pails of malted milk,

And gives them meatloaf made of mince
(The same as pies), and lots of quince;
In short, she thinks of every treat
That Santa's reindeer like to eat.

And every night at half-past ten
Out to the stable she goes again,
To see that the straw is smooth and deep
And all the reindeer fast asleep.

Day in, day out, till that special ride,
The impatient reindeer wait inside

And patient Mrs. Claus appears
To rub their noses and scratch their ears.

. . .

On Christmas Eve, great Santa's shout
Finally calls the reindeer out.
The sleigh is hitched, and the toys all tied
To keep them from falling over the side.

When everything's shipshape and everything's right
For that round-the-world trip in a single night,
Mrs. Claus, giving a wave of goodbye,
Watches them gallop into the sky;

Then, hanging a wreath on the frosted pane
To welcome her husband home again,
She takes up her candle and climbs into bed
With a goosefeather pillow under her head.

. . .

Yet on Christmas morning, while girls and boys
All over the world are opening toys,
Mrs. Santa herself has no present at all,
Not a single package no matter how small.

But she doesn't mind and she doesn't care
That nobody thinks of her anywhere—
For now on the wind she hears a whistle,
Faint as a star and light as a thistle,

The crack of a whip, and a jingling sound
As reindeer and runners skim to the ground!
Great Santa unhitches his world-weary team,
Gives them all soup-plates of cherry ice cream,

Stomps on the doorsill to shake off the snow,
Throws his wet mittens as far as they'll go,
And cries to his wife: "Merry Christmas, my love!
Can you guess what I've brought you? And what it's
        made of?

"I might have brought back this Christmas day
A burst of stars from the Milky Way,
A comet's tail or a planet's ring,
A moonbeam rubbed from a thrush's wing,

"A length of sky, to make you a coat,
Or a necklace of rainbows for your throat.
But the present I bring is rarer far,
More precious even than moonlight or star.

"It's made of the smile of a little boy
Who never before had a single toy;
It's made of children clapping their hands
In all the near and far-off lands;

"It's made of shouts and laughs and hails
In Italy, France and New South Wales;
It's made of one loud and long 'Hurrah!'
From icy Alaska to Zanzibar."

[169]

"I bring you this day of Jesus' birth
The joy of every child on earth!
A joy that the magic of outer space
Has fused to a gem and a sign of grace."

And reaching deep inside his jacket,
Santa takes out a tiny packet,
Wrapped in shreds of cloud and tied
With ribbons of lightning. "Look inside."

Now Mrs. Claus sets eyes upon
A diamond, flashing like the sun,
A diamond flashing with the joy
Of every Christmas girl and boy.

.   .   .

And out in the stable, munching hay,
Their next ride twelve whole months away,
The reindeer lift their heads to hear
The happiest laugh of all the year.

ALICE S. MORRIS

Christmas Morning

If Bethlehem were here today,
Or this were very long ago,
There wouldn't be a winter time
Nor any cold or snow.

I'd run out through the garden gate,
And down along the pasture walk;
And off beside the cattle barns
I'd hear a kind of gentle talk.

I'd move the heavy iron chain
And pull away the wooden pin;
I'd push the door a little bit
And tiptoe very softly in.

The pigeons and the yellow hens
And all the cows would stand away;
Their eyes would open wide to see
A lady in the manger hay,
If this were very long ago
And Bethlehem were here today.

And Mother held my hand and smiled—
I mean the lady would—and she
Would take the woolly blankets off
Her little boy so I could see.

His shut-up eyes would be asleep,
And he would look just like our John,
And he would be all crumpled too,
And have a pinkish color on.

I'd watch his breath go in and out,
His little clothes would all be white.
I'd slip my finger in his hand
To feel how he could hold it tight.

And she would smile and say, "Take care,"
The mother, Mary, would, "Take care";
And I would kiss his little hand
And touch his hair.

While Mary put the blankets back
The gentle talk would soon begin.
And when I'd tiptoe softly out
I'd meet the wise men going in.

ELIZABETH MADOX ROBERTS

Earth and Sky

(THEY TALK TO EACH OTHER ON CHRISTMAS EVE.)

EARTH. Oh Sky, you look so drear!
SKY. Oh Earth, you look so bare!
EARTH. How chilly you appear!
SKY. How empty you lie there!

SKY.	My winds blow icy cold.
EARTH.	My flowers have gone from me.
SKY.	Yet I've one Star of gold.
EARTH.	And I have one green Tree.

SKY.   I'll set my Star on high
Alone in its own light
For any Child to spy
Who wakes on Christmas Night.

EARTH.   I'll hang my Tree with toys,
Like fruit and flowers gay,
For little girls and boys
To pick on Christmas Day.

THEY
SAY TO-
GETHER   Then let the soft snow fall,
And let the cold wind blow!
We have in spite of all
A pretty thing to show;

Yes, Christmas Eve and Morn
We'll show our pretty thing
To every baby born
Of Beggar-man or King.

EARTH.	Oh Sky, you look so clear!
SKY.	Oh Earth, you look so fair!
EARTH.	How bright your Star shines here.
SKY.	How green your Tree grows there.

ELEANOR FARJEON

The Friendly Beasts

Jesus, our brother, kind and good,
Was humbly born in a stable rude;
The friendly beasts around Him stood,
Jesus, our brother, kind and good.

"I," said the donkey, shaggy and brown,
"I carried His mother up hill and down;
I carried her safely to Bethlehem town.
I," said the donkey, shaggy and brown.

"I," said the cow, all white and red,
"I gave Him my manger for His bed;
I gave Him my hay to pillow His head.
I," said the cow, all white and red.

"I," said the sheep with curly horn,
"I gave Him my wool for a blanket warm;
He wore my coat on Christmas morn.
I," said the sheep with curly horn.

"I," said the camel yellow and black,
"Over the desert upon my back,
I brought Him a gift in the wise man's pack.
I," said the camel yellow and black.

[175]

"I," said the dove from the rafters high,
"I cooed Him to sleep so He would not cry,
I cooed Him to sleep, my mate and I.
I," said the dove from the rafters high.

FRENCH CAROL

Long, Long Ago

Winds thru the olive trees
   Softly did blow,
Round little Bethlehem
   Long, long ago.

Sheep on the hillside lay
   Whiter than snow,
Shepherds were watching them,
   Long, long ago.

Then from the happy sky,
   Angels bent low
Singing their songs of joy,
   Long, long ago.

For in a manger bed,
   Cradled we know,
Christ came to Bethlehem,
   Long, long ago.

ANONYMOUS

Christmas Pageant

The third-grade angels, two by two,
March in, their cardboard wings askew.

A kindergarten shepherd skips;
A halo from its mooring slips.

The oriental kings, all three,
Wear Mama's costume jewelry,

While spotlights from each ribboned wreath
Accent the braces on the teeth,

And wise men, from the upper classes
Look *very* wise, in horn-rimmed glasses.

MARGARET FISHBACK

[177]

Author index

[181]

[183]

[185]

Title index

[189]